Beyond the
Chicken
the

Kelly Klober

Beyond the Chicken

A GUIDE TO ALTERNATIVE POULTRY SPECIES FOR THE SMALL FARM

Acres U.S.A.
Austin, Texas

Beyond the Chicken

Acres U.S.A.
P.O. Box 301209
Austin, Texas 78703 U.S.A.
512-892-4400 • fax 512-892-4448
info@acresusa.com • *www.acresusa.com*

Printed in the United States of America

Publisher's Cataloging-in-Publication

Kelly Klober, 1949-
Beyond the chicken / Kelly Klober. Austin, TX, ACRES U.S.A., 2014
xviii, 198 pp., 23 cm.
Includes index and illustrations
ISBN 978-1-60173-042-8 (trade)

1. Poultry. I. Klober, Kelly, 1949- II. Title.

SF487.KS 2014   636.5

CONTENTS

Eggs and Feathers

It seems that much of my life has been about feathers and eggs, eggs and feathers.

My grandmother raised canaries, and her kitchen was filled with song as she tended the little hens on their nests of minuscule eggs. One of my first clear memories is of being lifted up to view a pair of squabs that had hatched from two eggs about the size of the last joint of a man's thumb. Even my toys had an avian theme. There was the little plastic hen that, when pressed down on her spring-supported legs, would pop out a small, white, plastic egg. Most of these quickly disappeared into the dark void beneath our living room couch. Then there was the target game with the large red hen centered on a small bull's-eye. When the bull's-eye was hit with a suction cup–tipped dart, the hen would "lay" a ping-pong ball egg. These, too, soon vanished into the wilderness beneath our couch.

Small plastic parts and dart-shooting toy guns—yes, I was raised in the pre-childproof, totally politically incorrect era. Then, however, the only real harm done seemed to be when Dad stepped on one of my plastic farm animals during a barefoot, nighttime trip to the bathroom.

When it was announced that we were moving from the far suburbs of St. Louis to a real farm, I drew upon the vast cash reserves of a nine year old to buy a New Hampshire hen of uncertain years. I suspect she was of an age that allowed her to vote Ike in for his second term. And I didn't so much buy her as ransom her from a nearby poultrier that dressed such birds to order for the meat bird trade fifty-plus years ago.

The old girl actually had a little life left in her and laid a number of fair-sized eggs. Drawing on the wisdom contained in decades-old books borrowed from the library, I weighed, measured, and assayed those eggs with all of the passion a nine year old on a mission can muster. She made the transition to our new farm home but succumbed soon after. In the years since, I can truthfully say that I have owned at least a few of most every domestic poultry variety (I have forgone swans, but only after reading that early swan keepers could often be told by their missing fingers). I owed my early childhood health to a particular Gray goose my grandmother owned. When she took a mind to do so, she could chase me across our backyard in Olympic sprint time. And I was once nearly condemned to repeating the third grade for hiding an injured pigeon in my desk. It was a beautiful red-feathered bird retrieved from a window ledge during the lunch hour.

Bantams, ducks, geese, pheasants, pigeons, turkeys, and once a nomadic peacock—all have made their way to our poultry yard at one time or another. "Poultry yard" is a British term that I have picked up in recent years because it rather neatly ties together how poultry have been kept on farms and smallholdings. It is not a chicken yard as your grandparents or mine would have thought of it but rather an area of the farmyard, often a rather large area, where multiple poultry ventures are centered and the equipment needed for their care are based.

As agriculture has become more industrialized, the production of many poultry species has fallen to a relative handful of specialized producers. A handful of breeds were drawn on to build the modern poultry industry. When I was a young man, two of the largest four hundred farms in the United States produced naught but a strain of Pekin duck to be sold as Long Island duckling. Over the course of just my lifetime turkey production settled heavily on the Broadbreasted White and Bronze varieties and their production in buildings that house literally thousands of birds each. The Broadbreasted turkey has become a sort of megabroiler, producing massive amounts of white breast meat per bird. They have been developed to have such large breasts that they are no longer able to naturally reproduce. The large amounts of breast meat are used in all manner of processed foods and for institutional food services. The massive turkey hens are artificially inseminated every few days to produce fertile eggs to keep alive a system of production and a bird that would not otherwise survive. And survivability and its near twin, sustainability, were very much what poultry yards were about once and should be again. Early poultry yards were busy places, alive with activity and rich in variety.

A set of pictures recently crossed my desk depicting a farmer in Great

Britain in the early twentieth century loading out to move to a new farm. Pictured in the farmyard were several early flatbed farm trucks. On each, poultry coops were stacked three high. In the crates you could see several breeds of duck, large pigeons, chickens, and even pairs of swans.

Poultry has been kept for many reasons, from the production of meat and eggs to natural pest control, and even for their aesthetic appeal and sport. Homing pigeons are raced over substantial distances, there are competitions for pigeons that tumble and roll, geese were once fought like gamecocks, bantams in ever more varied colors and elaborate patterns are still being developed, and peafowl and some pheasants are aptly termed "ornamentals." I have read that peafowl were once regular table fare in royal halls and palaces, and they are of the pheasant family. Now they are largely the provenance of color breeders and modern rurbanites who buy a pair or two to serve as an animated, feathered topiary. We had a neighbor who kept peafowl around his house and offices for his family turkey business. They were a bit of vividly colored advertising for his farm business. He kept them until one rather large and aggressive peacock flew down from atop a building and did considerable damage to an unsuspecting hired hand. Another friend now keeps a couple hundred peafowl in several colors and travels the Midwest selling them at numerous bird markets. He has made a pretty neat little business of them.

And there, I believe, is the defining role for the use and keeping of many of these poultry varieties. I have likened them to what in the farm implement industry is termed the short or sideline trade: market niches for producers of a single implement, a line of small implements, or implements for very specific uses. They generate fair amounts of income, have not the potential to carry an entire operation, and complement other, existing arms of an operation. My friend's nice little peafowl business has grown to a point where he gives it substantial focus but not all of his time and resources. It was developed while he worked forty-plus hours a week off of the farm. Now he also raises rabbits, does some order buying as a part of his travels, and keeps other poultry varieties and some cattle.

Poultry ventures were typically fitted in and around other, often larger, farming ventures. A set of turkey hatchlings might be started prior to the early field work and then not marketed until late fall when added cash flow to the farm is usually lacking. There are indeed numerous seasonal aspects to poultry production, especially for those wishing to pursue day ranging or other facets of outdoor production. The choice of poultry varieties to produce can also be influenced by regional patterns of demand, producer skill sets and available facilities, the presence of necessary supporting infrastructure, producer likes and dislikes, and more.

Historically, these have never been large ventures on U.S. farms, and even a very few hundred of some of the larger varieties can make heavy demands on a farm or smallholding's resources. Our old neighbor with turkeys grew out one or two groups of about 2,500 Bronze turkeys each year while selling hatching eggs and poults, but they totally dominated that farm. This was over fifty years ago, and he had probably the largest investment in feed processing and handling equipment of any farmer in our township. For most of history, these alternative poultry varieties were kept first for the needs or pleasure of the producer's family. They often grew out of or next to other poultry-keeping ventures, and they made of these folks poultry producers/breeders rather than mere keepers of birds.

A farm venture, to be viable, does not have to produce tens of thousands of units, but it does have to yield a high-quality product to be in strong demand and garner good prices. Long before the term "range broiler" was on every foodie's lips, Amish and other small farmers in our area were producing frying chickens that cooked and tasted the way they remembered it.

A neighbor of ours a few farms over had been raising "natural" broilers, old-school fryers, for a number of years when he found a new venture to push the poultry envelope on his farm. He had been listening to those dissatisfied with too-large turkeys or who simply wanted something different than turkey during the holiday season. Late one summer he bought fifty Buff Orpington cockerel chicks and grew them out to about twenty-two weeks of age. He then marketed them as dressed birds of about seven pounds. It was a classic size and age for a roasting fowl, and they were a good fit for a number of consumers wanting an alternative to the holiday turkey that wouldn't challenge their cooking skill set. One of the definitions of eternity is two people and turkey leftovers. By simply listening to the people who were already buying one of his farm's products, he had found a new market for another. It never grew to be anything truly large, but it did produce some Christmas money for his family at a time when most cash flow onto a farm slows. He grew this venture to about seventy-five to a hundred birds per year and essentially grew them to fill repeat orders.

Such markets are generally quite local in nature, require an extensive investment in the direct marketing process on the part of the producer, and can absorb only modest numbers if good prices are to be maintained. You can sell way more two-dollar roasters than twelve-dollar ones, but doing so pays few bills.

Most of the alternative or specialty poultry breeds and varieties have a pricey, gourmet image with consumers, which can affect demand. I suspect that most consumers now have experience only with broiler chicken and, to a far lesser extent, turkey meat. And even with a broiler many people would not know how to disjoint and prepare a whole bird in any way beyond simple baking or frying. A duck, a goose, a turkey without a pop-up timer embedded in it, squabs, or game birds are simply beyond the ken of most consumers. They might joke about dining on squab, pheasant under glass, or quail on toast, but such things are as alien to most U.S. consumers as dining on African plains game.

The recent rising interest in natural and heritage chicken production has caused an uptick in interest in other winged varietals from the poultry yard. Interest, but interest backed with very little in the way of hard knowledge. At our local farmers' market there have been enough inquiries about squab to prompt one market family to invest in a few pair of pigeons of one of the squabbing varieties.

The commercial trade in squabs has been, for decades, dominated by a handful of producers on each coast. They sell directly to the few white-linen tablecloth restaurants that offer such unique fare as squab. For many years there was one pigeon "farm" in eastern Pennsylvania that maintained a thousand pairs of squabbing pigeons on a parcel of land measuring less than one acre.

At farm meetings and seminars and in a growing number of phone calls, I have been fielding all sorts of questions about alternative poultry ventures. Small family farmers and smallholders are seeing them as opportunities consistent with the historical role of producers in their area. Nearly all varieties have a limited upside: they will require the producer to become a knowledgeable breeder of such birds, depend almost entirely on the direct marketing process, will probably grow out of an existing venture on the farm, and the attempt should not be made to string too many poultry ventures together lest it skew the farm's overall course too far in a single direction. The poultry yard is, I believe, going to always be dominated first by egg-producing chickens and then meat-producing chickens.

One or two more allied ventures might be added, drawing from turkeys or waterfowl and to a lesser extent pigeons, guineas, game birds, or ornamentals. The producer of such birds will have to position himself as a knowledgeable hand able to provide backup support and supply birds of highest quality. He must rely almost entirely on the production of pure-bred birds, often purebreds with heirloom breeding status.

This corner has long advocated the importance of purebred livestock genetics to the family farm. Make no mistake about it, when a poultry variety is taken up to be produced for the practical ends for which it was developed it is livestock as defined by the law, the tax man, and the efforts of conscientious producers working for "the good of the breed." A purebred flock is self-perpetuating; it is the living, breathing definition of sustainability. It does not lock the producer into off-farm dependence on sources of the all-important, all-defining seedstock. It becomes up to the producer to tend the birds well, breed them better, and to be ever more productive to meet the demands of the market. Purebred birds also present the greatest number of marketing options, including sales of breeding stock and hatching eggs to other producers.

In recent days much, perhaps too much, has been made of rare and heirloom poultry varieties and the inflated prices that have been paid for some of them. Not long ago a trio of Chocolate Orpingtons was supposedly offered on the Internet for five thousand dollars with absolutely no word about how difficult this color is to maintain in a breeding program. Current poultry prices and demand have been likened to the exotic animal craze of a few years back, and a lot of folks do jump from one hot breed or variety to another.

These short, hot markets are termed "breeder" markets and last only briefly. They are fueled by the latecomers to a breed who hope to raise and sell a generation or two of birds that at least look the part before the fad for that breed or variety folds. The highly fecund nature of most poultry varieties keeps these bubbles of interest truly short-lived.

This kind of thinking made a mess of the farming of many types of nontraditional hoofed stock and has done much damage to many rare and heirloom chicken breeds. Preservationists are now having to go back and redo much of the work that they did restoring and thus popularizing certain breeds that went on to be overbred and with too many poor specimens entering their gene pools. Those early efforts not only raised awareness of certain breeds but greatly heightened demand for them. Such demand would fuel itself for a time. Many ill-prepared folks were drawn to the more challenging breeds, and inferior birds were kept and bred from. Some breeds are even now having to deal with questions of genetic purity.

Breeders are raising serious questions about the integrity of the gene pools for a number of minor breeds, and even a few of the more mainstream breeds. There is far more to a well-bred chicken with a buff color than the buff color alone. An acquaintance bought a set of Buff Plymouth Rocks from a well-advertised source only to find most of them arriving with incorrect leg colors, indicative of crossbreeding.

The interest in and continuing demand for heirloom varieties of poultry will continue only for as long as the purity of those gene reserves are protected and they are bred up to the performance standards set for those breeds. These standards were set most often by an earlier generation of farmer/breeders who saw the need to balance eye appeal with optimal economic performance. If you go to a hatchery catalog and order two of these, three of the others, and a couple with the funky feathering, you are doing naught but wasting potentially valuable genetics.

There has to be more to a plan of poultry ownership and care than owning some of those fancy birds the lady on the TV cooking show keeps on her country estate. They are living things, many of them badly in need of safeguarding and breeding up to former levels of utilization and productivity. Nearly every breed type trait was developed and refined initially for practical ends. Crests, one of the showiest traits, were originally cultivated to provide added protection for the comb and delicate head area in cold climates. Nevertheless, eye appeal itself is important. Studies have shown that the greater a variety's appeal to a potential producer, the higher the level of care it will receive from that producer. And eye appeal is certainly a factor in making sales.

Dad had a pretty good rule when I was growing up. If it was my money I could spend it on any venture I wanted to add to the farming mix, as long as I could answer two questions: How would I profit from it, and where or to whom would I sell it? Finding the answers to those two questions has guided my business plan for most of my life. Seeking those answers kept me on the farm, kept me out of the ostrich business, kept me gainfully employed, kept me from owning wallabies, and led me into the modern renaissance in poultry production from local farms and smallholdings. It has created in me a stubborn streak of practicality that has me weighing the costs, to the last penny, of every potential venture.

A lot of ink has been sloshed about in telling of the success of certain poultry ventures. Some truly eye-popping prices have been reported, and some of these price-gougers are being depicted as gentrified poultritiers. It is high-class gloss disguising the need for some heavy doses of reality.

Most of those über prices hinge on near-immediate access to upscale consumer communities with substantial levels of disposable income. In a more rural area both sales volume and pricing levels will be limited. As one veteran of our eastern Missouri bird markets puts it, "Ask those upscale prices out along the lettered blacktops, and one-third of the folks will remember when such things sold for much less at the local sale barn, one-third have a cousin or brother-in-law raising the same thing, and one-third will go home and raise it for themselves."

Our farmers' market is roughly seventy miles from the St. Louis area. For every ten miles you move closer to St. Louis, you can add twenty to thirty cents to the selling price of a dozen brown-shelled eggs. Cross into St. Louis County and you can ask for four to five dollars for a dozen and get it from some of the folks there. You have also added to your cost of producing those same eggs, however. There are added travel costs, more packaging and handling costs, and the additional time and effort it takes to reach and interact with these consumers.

Direct marketing means that you go where the consumers are or draw them to you with the type of production they prize. It puts more money in the producer's pocket but is generally limited to areas that are an hour or two's drive from the home farm. Thus they are true niche markets, capable of using only so much premium-priced production before being skewed or broken. Once broken these markets may not be possible to restore.

The producer can have substantial control over such a market, however. You must position yourself as a trusted figure in the market, emphasize quality, offer expertise and services as a part of your marketing plan, and control the amount of supply going into that market. Alternative poultry ventures on the family farm or smallholding have nearly always been modest in scope. They may have even been initiated just to feed the family. For example, a friend of mine keeps small flocks of very well-bred geese. Goose is a table favorite at his house. He has raised poultry of many types for most of his life, sells his birds widely, and participates in many different markets and poultry-themed events. Still, his geese are sold generally one, two, or three at a time, often as a handful of goslings or a small lot of hatching eggs. Mostly he sells small lots of started goslings and breeding pairs or trios. Not long ago I saw him sell a pair of young Brown African geese for one hundred dollars at a midwestern farm show. He had driven many miles to get there, as had the buyer. Over the three days of the show he fielded many inquiries about the birds that might lead to future sales. They were good birds, certainly worth the price, but it was not the kind of sale that could or would be made every day. With the modest number of birds from which he was breeding, to assure quality and not tax his facilities, he could not support a high volume of sales.

His flocks of large fowl chickens and beef herd–producing feeder calves are the primary ventures on his farm. He blends poultry and other pursuits for the diversity needed to assure him better risk management, extend and even cash flow, and to give his farm better environmental and economic integrity. Not everyone is going to want a goose for a holiday meal or budget for six-dollar-a-dozen organic eggs. It's rare to find someone who has the kitchen skills to prepare a brace of pheasants, the desire for the rich dark meat of squab, and/or the need and freezer room for a dozen heirloom-bred broilers.

Poultry ventures need to be carefully fitted together so as to not make the producer too dependent on a single venture group. Specialization is the methodology of the factory farm, which is certainly not in keeping with what modern consumers want and expect from local, artisanal agriculture. The independent producer needs to create a mix of ventures that complement each other, evens and extends cash flow, broadens markets, and more fully employs producer skills and labors.

Some years ago, as a part of a Sustainable Agriculture Research and Education (SARE) grant project, I assisted with a survey of poultry producers. The greatest majority reported keeping more than one poultry species. A good many kept up to three different species, but very few kept more than that. Most kept chickens, primarily large fowl, and the most common variety kept after that were turkeys. The next most common birds were waterfowl, generally ducks, and then guineas. Most were kept in modest numbers, secondary to the much larger chicken-based ventures. This is not unusual; chickens are the most commonly kept of livestock species in the world, kept in greater numbers than any other and by far more people.

Fried young guinea is a midwestern delicacy enjoyed in late summer and fall when the young of these very seasonally natured birds are to be had in greatest number. Most people have never eaten guineas, fried young or any other way, and know little about them other than what they read in a literature class on Ernest Hemingway, who shot wild guineas as a camp staple while on safari in Africa. I can remember when many of the farms in our region had a small flock of spotted Pearl guineas living a largely catch-as-catch-can existence. They were kept mostly for their amusing antics and pest control abilities, and many producers enjoyed their noisy nature, looking on them as feathered watchdogs. Now give most folks a young guinea and they will give it right back because they have no idea what to do with it. Most would do the same with a young Emden goose, a fine Pekin duck, a brace of Mondaine squabs, or a half-dozen quail. They're all worth keeping and propagating and can have a fairly substantial value, but not everywhere nor to everyone.

Perhaps the most critical letter I ever received for an article I had written was sparked by a piece about pigeon-keeping basics. The writer took me to task for perhaps making it sound too smooth and simple, a scenario akin to those raise-chinchillas-in-your-garage schemes of the 1950s. That was certainly not my intention, but pigeon keeping is a touchy point for a great many old feather hands. They were the first birds kept by a great many of us when we were youngsters. They are the hobby that many would love to grow into a business, but few have succeeded in this endeavor except in the rarest of instances. Most U.S. consumers have never even seen a squab offered, let alone eaten one. Many consider them little more than street vermin, and over the years pigeon keepers have become an ever more closed community.

I have fielded more questions about squabs and squabbing pigeons in the last two years than in all the fifteen before them. It may mean an emerging market: people who like range broilers and heirloom turkeys may be opening up to other poultry items. An emerging market is nearly always a delicate thing, and the first need will be for more education for consumers and producers alike. And the selling job will be huge. A squab is all dark, very rich meat. It is somewhat limited in the ways it can be prepared, and it will never be chicken-nugget cheap.

There is much pioneering to be done with most of these alternative species, whether generating markets or developing the necessary supporting infrastructure. Try to find two different sources of pigeon feeds in any small town in eastern Missouri. Many land-grant colleges no longer have poultry departments, there are very few poultry specialists left in extension work, and the new poultry keepers are divided into many camps, including some who are trying to housebreak or put clothes on their birds. It is an abomination to put a necktie on a turkey and then photograph the poor bird.

Among these ranks I do see emerging a cadre of modern poultry producers drawing heavily on the practices of poultry producers in the first half of the last century. Those were poultry men and women of a most practical bent applying some meaningful economic yardsticks to the production of their birds. They will be building upon flocks of purebred birds, relying on direct marketing, working with modest numbers of two or three different species, emphasizing quality over quantity, and are taking in hand and doing all of their own breeding up work. They see poultry as livestock, will model their flock building more and more after the work of purebred hoofed stock producers, and will be building up and forward by linking bird and breeder/producer from farm to market to the consumer's very doorstep.

The concepts behind modern hoofed stock production—performance testing, selective breeding, matching nutrition to performance—were done first in the production of poultry. Farmers came the closest to the long-dreamed-of weekly paycheck for their farming efforts with these birds.

Frankly, many thought that the modest-sized flock of family farm and smallholding poultry production was done, a thing of the past, along with buggy whips and shucking pegs. That it has come back so far and so fast has surprised a great many, including this old boy. In a very real sense we have been given a second chance with these birds. Still, producers beware. If we go wrong this time there will be no third chance, and some of these breeds will be lost to extinction along with the dreams of those who love them.

CHAPTER 1

The Chicken

Bantams, Heirlooms, and Easter Eggers

SILVER GRAY
DORKING

Poultry is kept and bred in a great number of species—and breeds and varieties within those species. If you ever find yourself with an hour or two to kill, stop by your local library and start a list of just pheasant varietals. To that list then add the pheasant pigeon and the old English large-fowl chicken breed, the pheasant fowl. Then track down all of the rumors about those who have tried to cross pheasants with chickens, guineas, and other fowl. Take most of those tales with a very large grain of salt, however. The pigeon and the hen have no blood ties to the pheasant, but these stories do indicate just how wide a loop you can throw in poultry production. It is a vast tribe with a great nomenclature. Yet there are those who would relegate chickens to just two groups: those for producing eggs and those to be fried up within a very few weeks of hatching.

Both are worthy ends, though I have long said I would much prefer the life of a pit-tried battle stag to that of a short-lived though pampered factory-farmed broiler. If you had a southern/midwestern rearing like mine, eggs and poultry meat were on your plate several times each week, morning, noon, and night. For my southern-raised grandparents fried chicken was a breakfast food. What has so impressed me of late are the many ways independent poultrymen and women have pushed the egg and poultry meat windows. Through breeding and marketing they have created rewarding new niches.

One example that quickly comes to mind is a neighbor who is a well-established breeder of Katahdin sheep. He turned to poultry production with a similar mind-set and largely the same skill set. To the task of producing select table eggs he has applied much of what he learned producing and marketing his new (on the U.S. scene) breed of hair sheep. In the St. Louis area a marketing opportunity has opened for cage-free, more naturally produced eggs. A family operating a large community-supported agriculture (CSA) program buys local eggs to include in their weekly bundles to extend their marketing year and hold customers through the winter months when produce is limited. Our neighbor began with a mixed flock of hens, brown-egg layers largely based on the Barred Plymouth Rock and Dominique breeds. He also had on hand a few "industrial" green-egg layers—Easter Eggers in some catalogs. Those green eggs caught the eyes of the city-based consumers, who began to ask for more of them. Those industrial Easter Eggers weren't the best layers, however, but our neighbor had an idea of how to improve the numbers. The green egg color is a dominant genetic trait, so he began building a flock of better-producing barred and green egg–laying breeds from the poultry genetics he had at hand. He followed the old poultry axiom that has now been attributed to legendary Barred Plymouth Rock breeder Mr. Ralph Sturgeon: "Whether preserving a breed or breeding up a flock, begin where you are with what you have at hand."

Our neighbor crossed the Rocks and Dominiques to produce birds with the body type and vigor needed for a day-ranging flock of layers. The Rocks gave him a good start with large egg sizes and reasonable levels of per-hen egg production. Both breeds produced medium-brown colored eggs, and when mated to a rooster from a green-shell line the resulting pullets would largely produce eggs of a deeper green hue. To further this trait, he selected his breeding males only from eggs of the best and clearest green hue.

His is still a work in progress, though he is stabilizing this green egg trait in a breeding line of barred birds with a good body type for day ranging. He will continue to selectively breed for increasing laying performance per hen and will have to carefully monitor shell color, always factoring it into breeding male selection. He is not out to create a new breed but rather to establish a breeding line that will produce for his market and perform well on his farm. As those traits become ever more fixed and consistent, his flock will move toward what would be termed breed status. This process is how so many of the new breeds were created early in the last century. He saw no role for these birds beyond his farm and market, but to become a more successful egg producer he chose certain traits to refine in his birds and thus became a true poultry breeder.

In a somewhat different vein, I recently became acquainted with a poultry producer in the Northeast following an equally imaginative breeding/marketing track. He lives in an area near a great many Italian-American communities with substantial levels of disposable income. To better sell to consumers and Italian-themed restaurants there, he chose to operate with poultry breeds with strong Italian-heritage factors. For meat bird production he chose birds of the Dorking breed, one of the most ancient poultry breeds, sometimes even referred to as the Roman chicken. For egg production he has chosen the Ancona breed, a colorful black-and-white mottled breed developed in Italy that lays great numbers of large, chalk-white eggs. The Dorking is bred in several colors and patterns, the Ancona is bred in a single and a rarer rosecombed variety. The Leghorn is another breed of Italian origin bred in a number of varietals, and I would not be surprised if he was harboring future plans for the Roman Crested goose variety. The Dorkings do not grow nearly as fast as today's factory-farmed Cornish-X broilers. That slower growth rate, however, does enable them to produce poultry meat with distinct qualities valued by many consumers. Meat color, texture, and flavor are enhanced by slower growth and the birds receiving more exercise. These are also the birds for which the Italian recipes and styles of cooking were developed.

They are then clearly the best choices to be used with the sauces, seasonings, and cooking times and methods associated with Italian cuisine. Similarly the black-skinned Silkie chicken breed is valued in the trade to upscale Chinese restaurants. Do similar markets await breeds of French origin for use in that cuisine, Spanish breeds for those tastes or breeds developed in the Caribbean for that style of food preparation?

Caribbean and other Latin cuisines are on the rise in this country, and not long ago an article in *Parade* magazine included the lament of a Caribbean chef on the lack of "tough" chicken. No, the chef did not want poultry meat with the texture of shoe leather. He was expressing the need for chicken meat with the texture (muscle tone) and flavor to work best with the long cooking methods, sauces, stews, and seasonings used in his style of food preparation.

The American Livestock Breeds Conservancy now defines a heritage broiler as one that reaches appropriate market weight no earlier than sixteen weeks of age and is from one of the pure breeds recognized by the American Poultry Association before 1950. That age factor assures some aging of the meat on the "hoof," better muscle tone leading to better eating texture or mouth feel, and a richer, real-tasting chicken.

The Ancona, though a white-egg layer, was recognized by the American Poultry Association in 1898 and is a heritage breed in every sense of the word. The entire Mediterranean grouping of large fowl chickens are white-egg layers with but a very few exceptions. Along with that other Italian breed the Leghorn, they are among the most prolific of the laying breeds. The white-shelled egg is the heritage egg for at least the last three generations of U.S. consumers, the egg with which they have been most familiar for the whole course of their lives. When my grandparents ran their egg route in the early sixties their primary selling tools were green and yellow mesh baskets filled with large, chalk-white Leghorn and Ancona eggs.

Beneath the shell all eggs are nutritionally the same, although there is some evidence for possible breed-based differences in taste and texture. Early French chefs went so far as to discern differences in eggs laid at different seasons of the year and created different recipes for them. Yes, an Ancona egg would mean more to an Italian-American consumer than perhaps an Irish-American or Asian-American consumer, but then this poultry keeping renaissance of ours is very much about finding and filling niches of need and want.

Poultry raisers are going to have to become much savvier about how they deal with surplus cockerels. Six male chicks are produced for every four pullet chicks hatched. It is a ratio that extends all of the way back to the feral Red Junglefowl, the genetic forebear of most modern fowl breeds. A lot of little cockerels are now simply euthanized upon hatching. This is especially true for the surplus males produced with the lighter weight egg-laying breeds and the numerous hybrids and sex-link crosses. Such males are relatively small, grow more slowly, and lack some of the carcass qualities associated with a good meat bird. Imaginative uses for these surplus birds have included sales to reptile keepers as feeder stock. I nearly shudder to think what the animal rights people might do if they decide to delve into the issue of surplus cockerel chicks and what is done with them.

As I write this the markets for range broilers and select brown-shelled eggs are beginning to plateau. Some of this has to do with an uncertain economy, but the bloom is leaving the rose for these items among some of the foodies, and producers have not been doing enough to bolster their flocks with selective breeding for improved and more efficient production. Some are waiting simply to jump to the next hot thing on the artisanal food/farming front, but if the next big thing is red deer or mammoth pumpkins their investments in poultry keeping equipment will go completely for naught. What is sorely needed now is a growing number of producers to take up these breeds and varieties with an approach that combines imagination and a true appreciation for the innate utilitarianism of these birds. The two classic methods of increasing sales and profits from any production are sparking greater demand or paring the costs to produce without affecting the quality of the output. In niche farming systems selling into local markets, producers can have much to say about the amount of production that reaches that market.

The good producers see these birds as a venture for the long haul and the markets for them as things to be cultivated. Let me make an off-the-wall point here: in a world full of cookies the commercial trade is dominated by the presence of man-made, factory fresh creations from Oreos to chocolate chip cookies. Yet the epitome of the latter cookie is the homemade, fresh-from-the-oven version made by many loving hands. Just because factory-made cookies are everywhere, it doesn't mean that there won't always be people who prefer the homemade variety. The success of the modern independent poultry producer hinges almost entirely on producing and maintaining the bonafides for a truly homegrown, tended-by-loving-hands bird. Not a game for modern family farmers and small-holders you say? What about all of those homemade cookies still being made? We can still produce our birds out among the trees and in the fresh air instead of in a factory.

For the last half century and more the Cornish-X broiler has been held out as the be-all and end-all for poultry meat consumers. A great many of those folks have little or no experience with roasting and stewing hens, chickens for baking, real Cornish hens, and capons, and they have little in the way of knowledge or skills to fully utilize a meat bird of any size.

Earlier I mentioned a producer marketing Dorking broilers to niche consumers. They are pricey birds to acquire, are far from the best layers, have the maintenance costs of a larger breed, and the producer has to invest substantial time and resources in their marketing. Some of this time he uses to explain to consumers how to most fully utilize the bird for which they have just given him a bit over twenty bucks. From one of his traditional broilers they should be able to produce three meals. The meatier parts first may go into a traditional chicken entree. The leftovers and trimmed meat might then be used in a stir fry, salad, wrap, or other sandwich preparation. The boney pieces can be used as a base for a rich soup.

The older hens that failed the culling process in my grandmother's flock went into soups, were baked, became chicken salad, or went into a big pot of chicken and dumplings. Those Reds, Rocks, and Orpingtons had substantial salvage value, and even the supermarkets back then sold stewing and baking hens. A friend that maintains a hatchery breeding flock for one of the heavier chicken breeds has a waiting list for the hens culled at the end of the hatching season. Those older, colored hens are highly valued by the Hispanic consumers in his area that use chopped poultry meat in all manner of recipes and preparations.

USDA poultry standards document many categories of chicken to be harvested for meat. These range from the diminutive true Cornish hen to roasting fowl of both substantial age and size.

There are opportunities to be found if one is attentive to the consumer and open to new ideas. As the local foods trend further unfolds, demand for poultry meat from breeds with strong regional identities should grow. New Hampshires and Plymouth Rocks in the Northeast, Wyandottes in the Upper Midwest, Buckeyes in Ohio, and other breeds with a regional history will rise in demand. Where Latino and Caribbean consumers are being served, breeds like the Cubalaya might find added favor and demand. Just as breed-specific beef and pork have found heightened acceptance and demand, the same could and should emerge with breed specific poultry meat.

On the egg production side, the brown-shelled egg is also in a time of transition and reevaluation. The brown-shelled egg emerged a few years ago, first, as something of a novelty; second, as an egg for the "super size me" generation; third, as a link to farming's past and heritage; and fourth, as a pillar of freshness and style for the foodies. There is validity in all four of those points, but eggshell color has virtually naught to do with an egg's content, how it was produced, where it came from, or the uses to which it can be put.

Producers really need to begin thinking more seriously about eggs, the logistics of their production, and how to add value to them. For the moment the brown-shelled egg may be the Cadillac of hen fruit, but most of the consuming public has far more experience with white-shelled eggs. Everything that adds value to a brown-shelled egg—organic feeding, cage-free production, day ranging—can be employed in the production of white-shelled eggs, too. And they are easier to dye at Easter time.

The economics of feeding, rearing, and containing clearly favor the white egg–laying breeds. The white-shelled egg in large and medium sizes is produced by a number of smaller, easier-to-maintain breeds that will generally outproduce most of the brown egg–laying breeds, and by a substantial measure. We can fit and feed at least three Brown Leghorn hens in the same space and for the same amount of feed as needed by two of our larger Buff Orpington hens.

The difference in egg sizes is but a fraction of an ounce between extra large, large, and medium eggs. That nomenclature refers just to egg size and has nothing to do with the quality of the eggs. Quality factors are denoted by letter grades of AA, A, and B.

The Hamburg breed, a smaller, active, and easier keeping breed, produces large numbers of medium-sized white-shelled eggs. The breed has even been dubbed the Dutch Every Day Layer. The Hamburg is just one example of a white egg–laying breed that brings economic factors to the table that simply can no longer be overlooked in light of modern feed grain prices. They are one of the breeds that, to me, epitomizes both the challenge and the answer to building a long-range future for independent, local, and artisanal foods producers. Such breeds offer a way to pare costs without sacrificing quality but challenge producers to do a better job of marketing and educating consumers. That good chalk-white egg is what built the poultry industry, and bringing it back to the marketplace in varied forms may well be the task that makes this poultry renaissance of the moment the lasting thing we all want it to be. Egg marketers are growing in their levels of savvy, and some very creative things are being brought to the marketplace now. The arrival of clear plastic egg cartons came almost at the same time as the emergence of interest in eggs with intensely dark brown shell color.

The clear carton makes shell color again a high-profile selling point, although they are a rather expensive packaging option when compared to the paper pulp carton preferred by many consumers on environmental grounds. A few producers have borrowed from their breakfast competitor, the cereal trade, and are offering a "variety pack" based on eggshell color. Into a twelve-egg carton they might place four brown eggs, four white eggs, and four green eggs; or six light brown eggs and six dark brown eggs. Where eggs of a single color are being packaged, it is key that they vary very little, if at all, in the way of color and size.

Also emerging are eggs offered in cartons of fewer than twelve eggs. Most of these are cartons of six or eight eggs and are a good fit for today's smaller families and the growing number of older Americans and single-person households. There is now even an eight-egg carton in a flower head configuration.

Every food staple will, from time to time, benefit from a bit of rethinking. Chicken meat was once far more than fried bits and pieces sold in a cardboard tub, and there is far more to a good egg than just shell color. Poultry producers now must bring imagination and initiative to the tasks of market building and paring costs to produce.

Another avian conundrum to be unwound, one on a par with that old chicken-or-the-egg poser, is the blue/green egg question.

Blue or green eggshell color is a very strong genetic trait in domestic fowl and can be bred on identifying traits widely separate from others. Just as with the white-shelled egg, the blue or green color goes all of the way through the shell. This is not true with the brown-shelled eggs, and with the darkest of the brown eggs the color must have some time to set after laying before the egg is handled.

Right now there is a swirl of names and appellations being applied to the birds that produce green- and blue-shelled eggs, and much confusion has been the result. Most commonly these birds are termed Araucanas, but honestly, very few folks have seen a true Araucana chicken. They are the breed of the New World, of South America, with their earliest origins perhaps lost forever in the mists of time.

Araucanas are rumpless fowl, have pendecules (fleshy growths with feathering attached to the head, not muffs or feather beards), and lay vivid blue eggs. They are also one of the most challenging chicken breeds. As they are a rumpless fowl there are considerable problems with matings being completed and egg fertility. Because of their near tropical origins they need good winter housing, and there is a very shallow breeding pool of these birds from which to draw on. They also carry a lethal gene causing about a fourth of the embryos to die in the shell around the eighteenth day of incubation.

A male hatched from a blue- or green-shelled egg will produce substantial numbers of pullet offspring that will go on to produce distinctively colored green eggs. When bred to brown egg–laying hens he will produce pullets that will lay darker green eggs. Breed to white egg–laying birds and the resulting pullets should produce eggs of similar though lighter hue. Such birds would be green-egg layers, but they aren't Araucanas. The term most often applied to them now is Easter Eggers. No standards have been set down for them as to size, breeding, conformation, or color. They are a pretty motley group and are far from being a breed or even a line that can be counted on to breed or produce with any sort of dependability. If it is just the ability to produce green eggs that makes an Araucana an Araucana, we had one with a wide bill and webbed feet and that produced ten little ducklings this spring.

Much hard work has gone into the creation of a breed called the Ameraucana, which was recognized by the American Poultry Association in 1970. They have a tail and feather muffs and a beard rather than pendecules adorning the head. A mature male of this breed will weigh six and a half pounds, a hen five and a half pounds. The facial muff and beard will form three separate lobes, wattles are very small, feet and shanks will be slate or blue, and they have a pea comb. And they are bred in very distinctive colors and patterns including Black, Blue, Blue Wheaten, Brown-Red, Silver, Buff, Wheaten, and White. They must breed true to those colors.

Over the years the terms Araucana and Ameraucana have been used, shall we say, a bit too freely. And it has added to the murkiness that has tripped up so many entering into modern poultry production.

In recent months I have become aware of at least two flocks of several hundred birds each being put together to produce these distinctively colored eggs for sale. There is substantial demand for select table eggs of distinctive color, but they must also be of good size, uniform in their appearance, and cost effective to produce. Both of these producers have had problems assembling green egg–layers in the desired numbers and with dependable levels of production. One was discussed earlier with his breeding program to create a much more dependable green egg–laying strain for his farm. The other, a young Amish farmer, bought several hundred hatchery-run Easter Egger pullets. He has since encountered all sorts of problems with levels of production and uniformity in the eggs produced. They were gimmick chickens, and you cannot build a business on a gimmick.

Both producers will have to breed their way up to better levels of egg-laying performance and to further stabilize the breeding lines with which they are working. To the best of my knowledge the green-egg layers have never had any extensive selective breeding for per-bird egg-laying performance. Improving performance and consistency of quality in the eggs produced will take time, a great deal of time. The Ameraucanas took time to develop even with Araucana genetics in place to draw upon.

Initially, a good breeding/producing flock is put together one good bird at a time as those birds are located and the best matings for them developed. It is the producer's responsibility to follow that possibly oldest rule of good livestock breeding: breed the best to the best to produce a new generation that will outperform the one before it.

There are other chicken varieties besides the large fowl that over the years have been put to some important economic uses.

One early method of producing a one-serving sized "Cornish" chicken was to cross White Cornish banty roosters with White Plymouth Rock miniature hens. Perhaps the place to begin this discussion is with a bit of terminology. "Bantams" are diminutive fowl with mature weights of less than thirty ounces per bird (often well under thirty ounces) and that exist in no other form. Miniature fowl are the scaled-down form of the large fowl breeds, often bred down directly from them.

The true bantam breeds include the Sebrights, Rosecombs, Booted, Quail, and Japanese. There is a miniature counterpart for most of the large fowl breeds, although they are not always exact duplicates in miniature. The miniature Welsummer, for example, does not produce nearly as dark-shelled an egg as its large fowl counterpart.

When I was a youngster few were the farms of the Midwest that did not have a flock of barn banties. They were little half-wild chickens that lived a catch-as-catch-can existence, surviving on what they could catch in their beaks or snatch from their barnyard environment, including spilt grain. They weighed a bit more than the diminutive purebreds and colored up like a litter of speckled cur pups. They might have topknots, feathered boots, and a few colors that you wouldn't find even in a big box of crayons. Some of them actually became established as landraces of sorts in different geographic regions. Up and down both the Missouri and Illinois sides of the Mississippi River a speckled bantam with a millefleur pattern of sorts emerged when I was a small boy. They would have flecking or a red, buckskin, or (rarely) white base. Some had a smallish topknot, and they would range in size from hens that would fit snugly in your hand to those pushing three pounds per bird. I suspect that they were one or another variant of the Speckle bantam taken up of late.

The first question raised about these diminutive fowl is, "Of what good is a little chicken?" Certainly they are ornamental and have been taken up by many exhibition breeders for the challenge some of the colors and feathering patterns in bantams represent. And, for some, there is the challenge to produce a perfect large fowl in miniature. For the backyard poultry folks the little birds take up less space, there is a reduced noise level, some of the breeds are exceptionally docile, they are easier to contain, they are bred in great variety, and they eat much less. Three bantam eggs will replace two large fowl eggs in most recipes and as a serving size.

Our barn banties would begin taking to the nest in early spring, and we once had one small hen emerge from the hayloft with five little peeps on Christmas Eve. A few times each year we would make a late-night safari to the barn with burlap bag and flashlight in hand. There we would pluck surplus birds—mostly roosters—from rafters, gate tops, stall walls, and other roosting places. My grandparents would then dress the contents of two or three cackling, wriggling, and occasionally even crowing tow sacks. Mostly they went into big pots of winter day vegetable soup or chicken and dumplings. The latter was a favorite of Dad's and one time, unbeknownst to us, she added a tray of store-bought chicken necks to a couple of the little roosters going into a big pot of dumplings. The second day into that particular pot Dad began his table grace by asking to be spared, in the future, from little banty roosters that were all neck.

In Europe bantam eggs and other exotic eggs such as those of ducks are regularly offered in stores. They obviously appeal to one- and two-person households that do limited cooking at home. And they could be said to be nature's way of controlling serving sizes.

I once set about the goal of owning a flock of miniature fowl counterparts for every one of the large fowl breeds we owned. In hindsight it was a sort of fool's errand as the small breeds are not supported by high demand in our area, and good seedstock for them costs every bit as much as good large fowl stock.

Rising grain and other feed costs have certainly sparked new interest in bantams and miniature fowl. However, their smaller size requires that they be given very nutrient-dense rations to maintain condition due to the small amounts of feedstuffs that they are able to consume. Many keeping them have opted to offer the higher protein content and higher priced game bird feeds to them.

There are some miniatures that can have practical applications of a sort. A well-bred Cornish miniature is quite a little chunk of meat in the hand. And some lines of Leghorn miniatures do lay well. And, where it is still desired or needed, miniature fowl are one of the most dependable choices for natural incubation. Cochin and Wyandotte bantams and their crosses have performed especially well in this role.

You can't turn a broody hen on or off as needed, and the broodiness factor has largely been bred out of the various large fowl breeds. It is an economic fact of life that the broody hen on the nest is not producing eggs. Miniatures and bantams do tend to be more seasonal in both their laying and brooding patterns, however. There are some management practices that are said to foster broodiness in chickens. These include lowering light levels in the housing and decreasing protein levels in daily rations. Nothing is sure, and you cannot force a bird's nature.

The above two breeds and a few others have a larger mature size and are thus able to successfully cover more eggs during incubation. With the Cochins, however, there is the matter of their feather-booted feet and legs. Such feathering makes it more difficult to keep the nests and eggs clean. The booted hens may even flip eggs out of the nest if their feet are heavily feathered. Such feathering can be trimmed, but many prefer to cross up the little birds to breed away such feathering and produce some larger females. Many purebred flock owners will keep a second flock of crossbred broodies and entrust some of their most valuable eggs to them. Crossing Cochins with Wyandottes or other, larger, clean-legged miniatures will breed out much of the leg feathering.

I suspect that the role and value of bantams and miniatures is only going to grow as more consider adding a few chickens to the backyard and aging baby boomers look for new pursuits in retirement. For many they will be a pleasant hobby, for some—such as color and show breeders—they will be a challenging exercise, and for others they will be a way to gain some control over what is coming into their homes and on their tables.

Many of the bantams and miniatures are quite docile, easily tended by children and older folk. Some are so docile as to not even show a tendency to fly up even to a low roost and thus are termed floor bantams. They bed down at night on coop floors, can be contained with simple fencing, are very quiet in nature, and are not in the least bit flighty.

Some of the very first very well-bred chickens that I owned were Single Combed Rhode Island Red bantams. They came from noted western Missouri poultry breeder, Mr. Morgan Craven, and were a delight to own. I kept several breeding trios in decked coops and would often notice my very practical-minded grandparents just standing, watching the little birds as they strutted and preened. Their little eggs had an almost jewel-like quality. The miniatures were often bred down from their large fowl counterparts or were put together from the miniature counterparts of the breeds that were used to create the large fowl varieties. One account is that along with selecting for smaller specimens the selected large fowl eggs would be set to hatch rather late in the year. With the shorter days, less daylight, and cooler temperatures to contend with, the birds did not develop to such a large size. Gradually, they could be bred down to a size with a mature weight in the bantam fowl range. And while there is only so much that you can put into a smaller package, there are some practical roots that can be drawn upon and cultivated with many of these small birds.

There is a tremendous amount of eye appeal with many of the smaller birds, and they do a pretty good job of selling themselves when displayed to the public. A lot of poultry people producing on commercial levels keep one or another of the bantam or miniature breeds for the challenge of producing something elite in type and appearance. The little birds were never kept in huge flocks, but a new role may be emerging for some producers of the more productive lines in modest numbers. The backyard chicken people have a very real need for producers of quality stock—

particularly started birds in which the sexes can be clearly and easily discerned. Such birds will have substantially greater value than hatchery-run, as-hatched bantam chicks if they can be marketed into areas where there is a demand for them.

Such folks need not just good birds in small numbers but also much in the way of support and information as to how to care for their birds. If they can find people who can answer their questions and provide them with good birds, they will then continue to patronize them. And savvy producers are beginning to market what they know, first in the price of their birds and then in what they can provide in the way of follow-up sales and support. There are chicken varieties that push the production envelope in many different ways and are deserving of consideration by at least modest numbers of producers seeking something beyond the basic egg or broiler. None will, I believe, be growable to major proportions, but they are becoming more identifiable in the marketplace.

Earlier I touched on the subject of natural incubation, and the hands-down choice of bird for this task is the Silkie. It is said that they would try to hatch porcelain doorknobs if presented with a nest of them. I once had a little White Silkie hen settle down on an empty nest on Labor Day and hold to it until Christmas Day. They are a bird that fits no handy category. They have fine, hair-like feathering, mulberry-hued skin, and black flesh, and they are too large to be a bantam and too small to be termed a large fowl. They are a bird of the East; Marco Polo encountered chickens with hair-like feathering on his fabled travels. Some are endeavoring to develop breeding lines of Silkies of larger size. This would enable the broody hens to cover more eggs and add to their worth in the upscale Chinese restaurant trade.

The Silkie is most commonly seen in the white variety, and some old hands hold that this is the only real deal Silkie. It is the variety sought out in the Asian food trade. They must have mulberry-hued skin, face, and wattles. When cooked the Silkie presents on the plate with black skin, meat, and even black bones. This is highly desired in the high-end Asian restaurant trade, where half of a Silkie is considered a one-plate serving. Not long ago *Time* magazine did a feature article on the growing interest in black foods, and one of the featured pictures was of a portion of black chicken, a Silkie I have to believe. Certain Asian-Americans also attribute medicinal properties to the flesh of the Silkie.

I have an acquaintance in eastern Pennsylvania that grows out four hundred White Silkies two to four times a year for sale into the Asian markets in New York City and Philadelphia. He markets them at about eighteen weeks of age for a price of a bit over four dollars a pound, live weight. He does report problems with locating chickens in sufficient numbers at one time and with the ability to grow to a desired market weight. The Silkie is not supposed to have any conventional feathers, and the purebred White Silkie is the one my friend must produce to hold his market and the premium price it pays. Not long ago, at a 4-H event, I had the sad task of informing a little girl that the "Silkies" she had acquired were of dubious breeding. Several had vividly red faces and wattles and showed traditional feathering in the wings and sides.

At local farmers' markets Silkies draw much interest and generally sell very well, especially started and young breeder trios of birds. They are one of the most difficult chickens to sex visually, and the standard answer to how to discern males from females is to wait until the young males begin to crow. Some hold that the combs on young females will have something of an indented appearance, but it is a challenge to work through the crest to make such a determination. I offer it here only as something for producers to trial with their own flock.

They are an easy breed to contain, very docile, but they will need some added protection from the elements and will not handle dampness. We have had best results with Silkies keeping them in elevated housing with wooden floors and access to all-wire sun porches on pretty days. They are rather poor layers, and if even a couple of eggs accumulate in the nest it may spark broodiness.

The large fowl Game chickens, the Pit fowl, are a hot button issue but deserve consideration because of their history, the strong genetic resource they represent, and their ability to thrive and perform in harsh and varying conditions.

Few are the livestock species that have been bred pure and so carefully for so long as have the Pit Games. Possibly only thoroughbred horses have been selectively bred longer. I will not argue the meaning or the morality of the fighting pit here, but the birds themselves are a broad and beautiful genetic resource that has been drawn upon to create many different chicken breeds.

The Games have been bred over the centuries in a great number of varieties and have continued to survive and even prosper long after the pit was outlawed both here and in many places abroad. They are most vigorous birds, hardy, easy keepers, and with many practical applications to them. Many have kept large-fowl Games to provide natural incubation for numerous other avian species. Many keepers of the rarer pheasant varietals have kept flocks of Games to provide a more manageable, natural incubation method for their most valuable and delicate eggs and then brooding for the hatchlings. And Game fowl breeding has gone into the creation of a great many different poultry breeds, such as that American classic the Rhode Island Red.

When I was more active in the preservation breeding of very rare, old breeds I encountered many who spoke of using small infusions of Game fowl breeding to bolster old and badly depleted breeding populations. Some even tapped back into the Game blood that had been used to originate a breed. These are truly venerable birds of great age, and certain patterns—such as the Black Breasted Red—can be used more easily to bolster a failing breed. The Black Breasted Red is the color pattern of the Red Junglefowl from which most modern fowl are descended. I have heard reliable sources say that if you opened all of the cages at a major poultry show, sealed the hall's doors for four years, and then opened them, all of the young would emerge with the Black Breasted Red pattern. A Black Breasted Red patterned Game hen bred to a pure male of the breed being restored will produce a strong pullet base from which to begin rebuilding. For five more generations breed the retained females to purebred males of the breed being preserved and the renewed flock can be considered pure to that breed. That little flicker of Game fowl fire will continue there, however, and will help to keep those old and endangered genes going forward.

The eggs of the Games are said to be some of the richest and most flavorful of all chicken eggs, and if those claims can be substantiated they will grow substantially in demand and value. And the birds are pretty fair layers with rather modest maintenance costs.

They represent just too rich a historical resource to simply let go. They're not a bird with which to launch a major venture, but they are the birds that were once owned and prized by kings and presidents. Abraham Lincoln proudly included on his résumé his role as an impartial judge of cockfights. Here is, I believe, an opportunity in feathers, with strain names like Democrats and Clarets that are waiting for imaginative breeders and marketers. They are the "heirloom breed" of heirloom breeds, and they bring an element of color and dash that has long been lacking in the poultry sector.

∞

Yes, there is far more to the chicken than the fried egg and the drumstick. Size, feather color, sex, seasonal availability, and more are now factors in how, where, and for how much a chicken is sold.

A friend thought he had found an outlet for the surplus males from his well-bred flock of LaFlèche fowl. They were large, solidly made birds with the black feathering valued by some ethnic groups. He traveled to a Sunday flea market attended by many folks who gathered to study his birds and then turn away. The split comb of the LaFlèche breed gave the birds a certain satanic appearance that those consumers found repugnant.

I have some friends that keep and highly value some exotic chicken breeds such as the Saipan and the Aseel. They were developed in hot and humid Asia and are quite primitive looking birds with roots as fighting stock. They endure, have value, and may yet have a further role to play.

In the lower Midwest, where we are, black-feathered birds can be a hard sell because of heat issues and the sameness of their appearance. In very cold climes, however, black-feathered birds are valued for their ability to cope with cold weather and make the most of limited sunlight. And white-feathered birds, while a personal favorite of mine, are viewed as being just too plain vanilla for folks dazzled by all of those hatchery catalog pictures of exotics, pictures that, by the way, are generally artist renditions and all but impossible to approximate in the real world.

Opportunities are being found now for poultry producers, and progress is being made one small flock at a time, just as it should be. At an Acres U.S.A. conference a few years back I met a young Amish farmer from a Colorado region not noted for poultry production. He had been selling some Cornish-X broilers into an upscale community there but had been looking for something to broaden that base and increase income. To that end he had bought a small box of Dark Cornish cockerel chicks with which to test out a theory. He had gone back to the very roots of the Cornish-X broiler to re-create and re-market one of the classic meat bird options of old. He had a bird that grew like a real chicken, and that growth pattern produced a better meat product that looked as it should on the plate and, dare I say, tasted like a chicken should.

Such pursuits will, I believe, only grow in number. Let me cite but one instance worth watching. The growing interest here in the Light Sussex breed, the historic meat bird or table fowl of England, will soon be creating a place in the marketplace or will quickly fade away. It is a white-skinned, white-shanked bird and thus something to which those of us who grew up with the yellow shanks and skin of the Rocks and Reds are not accustomed. Still, its cousins the Speckled Sussex and the Buff Orpington have long been known here. If a demand can be built here, they and other English breeds might follow the Light Sussex through on this growing wave of popularity. Those who love the Light Sussex breed are going to have to promote its real-world, practical values. Without them there will be no justification beyond the novelty factor for keeping and propagating them.

While the frankenfood people are trying to restructure and flavor soy and muscle "tissues" to look like and taste like chicken, the really wise thing may simply be to try to do more with real chicken.

CHAPTER 2

The Turkey
Beyond Thanksgiving

TURKEY

Benjamin Franklin considered it the noblest of all farm fowl, a bird better suited to be our national emblem than the American Bald Eagle.

The turkey and the Muscovy duck are the domestic fowl of the New World. The turkey has long been the first choice of entrees to center the table at the big holidays at the end of the year. The meat of the Broadbreasted, factory-farmed birds is being chopped and restructured to be used in everything from nuggets to hotdogs and luncheon meats.

Many would question the value Franklin placed on the turkey due to so many having sad experiences with the Broadbreasted White and Bronze varieties bred for micromanaged life in confinement housing. Those birds can no longer even naturally reproduce; that Thanksgiving turkey that needs a pop-up timer to guide inexperienced consumers was produced via artificial insemination due to the monstrous disproportions to which it is now bred. The Broadbreasted poults are still the most available at farm supply and feed stores, but watching even a handful of these grow and consume volumes of feed and then not produce any young has quelled many a would-be producer's desire to raise turkeys. It is perhaps the ultimate example of what can be termed a man-made food item.

Due to their sad experiences with these gobbling hothouse orchids, many country folk have come to believe that turkeys hatch looking for a place to just lie down and die. My first venture into turkey production was with a dozen Broadbreasted Bronze poults bought to be a summer project while I was still in grade school. I raised two of the twelve, we ate both of them, and my progress as a turkey raiser was a topic at the family table for many holiday meals to follow. My kid sister was in a picky eater phase at the time, and she ate 100 percent of the drumsticks produced in my first turkey crop.

Decades later, the interest in heirloom chicken breeds and range-produced broilers has also revived interest in the turkey as something more than a blob of white meat perched atop two unsteady legs. The heritage turkey varieties have survived to be again taken up and made into something special and apart from the factory-farmed turkey.

Smaller turkeys are being deep fried on back porches and balconies, the heirloom turkey has considerable panache among foodies and food writers, and the more naturally produced turkeys have been given considerable added value by the local and Slow Food movements. Many heirloom turkey varieties such as the Bourbon Red and the Narragansett have strong regional associations, and the Royal Palm, smaller Beltsville

Whites, and even the Midget White produce meat birds more in keeping with today's smaller families and fewer meals eaten at home.

For a long time it was believed that there was just one domestic turkey existing in a number of color and size varietals. All will freely interbreed. Recent research has shown some slight genetic differences in the backgrounds of some varietals such as the Black and the Slate. They were all derived from the wild turkey, which does exist in numerous forms. Varietals include the Eastern, Merriam's, Rio Grande, and Osceola. A colorful variant from Central America, the Ocellated turkey, is a much smaller bird, unique in its coloring and with distinctive red legs. Some folks are even finding their market niches raising one of the wild varieties, although they require special permits to possess and breed and may subject the producer to on-farm inspections from a state wildlife agent. Contact your local wildlife or conservation agency before acquiring any of these birds.

The most commonly seen heirloom varieties of turkey are the Bourbon Red, Royal Palm, Black (sometimes called Black Spanish), Slate, and Narragansett. Less often seen are the Buff, Auburn, Blue Royal Palm, Holland White, and Lilac. There are others, including a chocolate-hued variety with a long history as a bird of the South that could soon enjoy a big upswing since chocolate is the current hot color in poultry circles.

The small farm stalwarts are the Bourbon Red, Royal Palm, Black, and Narragansett. The last of these was long kept to naturally incubate eggs from other turkey and fowl varieties. The Royal Palm was recognized by the American Poultry Association in 1977, but its distinctive black-and-white coloring with black bands on the tail and coverts make it one of the most recognizable of the turkey varieties. Its weight of seventeen pounds for a young tom and ten pounds for a young hen make it a handy-sized bird for the small acreage and smaller consumer families.

A few years ago we had one pair of Royal Palms produce fifty-one poults in a single breeding year. They were also truly easy keepers, staying quietly within a pen made with fifty-four-inch-high cattle panels, and we found a fairly ready market for poults, young breeding birds, and even a few table birds at the local farmers' markets.

The Black, Slate, Bourbon Red, and Narragansett all have the same weight standards. They are twenty-three pounds for young toms and fourteen pounds for young hens. Old toms will cross the scales at thirty-three pounds and old hens at eighteen pounds. The Bourbon Red was sanctioned by the American Poultry Association in 1909 while the other three received their sanctioning all the way back in 1874.

The White Holland and the Beltsville Whites predate the Broad-breasted White and are heirloom white birds with all of the desirable dressing qualities associated with white feathering (cleaner dressing, fewer noticeable pin feathers). Rather than catalog all of the available color varieties here, suffice it to say that there is something for everyone. Varieties like the Slate or Lilac can offer true challenges to the color breeder, and interest in the different colors and patterns has certainly waxed and waned over the years. Vivid coloring has become a marketing factor for many working with the heirloom birds, but for lasting success the birds must be taken up and carefully bred for ever-improving growth rate and feed efficiency. These are big birds, and during the growing stage of their development they will, like my grandfather used to say, have to be fed with a scoop shovel.

A lot of folks have been eyeing a turkey venture after reading accounts of a handful of producers that have sold individual meat birds for three-figure prices. It is a bird highly prized by many, but economic realities will greatly limit selling opportunities at that price level or one anywhere close to it. The heirloom turkey is a different bird both on the farm and on the plate, and if grown slowly and given ranging opportunities, it will produce a most flavorful and distinctive poultry meat. To crack that ultra high-dollar market, breeders will have to overcome many challenges, however. Typically turkeys aren't truly local markets and will require: the producer to arrange for processing that will allow shipment (often by priority mail) across state lines, the facilities needed to hold and then ready the birds, a packaging system, and a marketing plan adequate to reach across substantial distances.

Some of the more publicized turkey ventures have had the benefit of support from breed preservation and food issue groups. Advertising, packaging, special slaughter and processing, dry ice for shipping, mailing costs, and other costs far beyond feed and housing have to be covered if producing for sales across a wide area. And these kinds of costs will take a big bite out of even three-figure selling prices. Four out of every ten hours given over to such a venture, especially during the early years, must be put into to the marketing process.

A producer of our acquaintance here in the Show-Me State had all kinds of problems with his attempts to market a large flock of heirloom turkeys. The flock numbered several hundred, all targeted for the holiday season. The one processor of poultry with the capacity our friend needed was three states away and had hundreds of birds to get processed, sold, and shipped within a very short window of time, and holiday turkeys are a true sell-it-or-smell-it venture. Our friend is no longer in the turkey business.

One of the few things I did right with my first turkey venture was to start with a very modest number of birds: twelve. My biggest mistake was thinking about producing turkeys by the hundreds, if not the thousands, before I had mastered caring for the twelve. With the small number I was able to gain skills and experience with very modest risk. The two birds that survived were readily absorbed by the market closest at hand, but had all twelve survived I would have run out of aunts and uncles before I ran out of turkeys. And with that as my marketing plan I was in trouble from the get-go.

A turkey is one of the truly big-ticket food items that is widely consumed, and especially so if the producer has added value in forms such as range rearing, organic feeding, or working with heirloom stock. They will add to production costs, but what's there not to like about a bird produced in such a manner? Well, there is that "finding room for it in the family budget" thing. Thus early sales may be quite few, and they will tax a local market if pricing is too high. Though business may grow out of sales of related items such as eggs or broilers, this is going to be a one-bird, one-sale-at-a-time venture, and quite slow to grow as a result.

A buyer of range broilers will know better what to do with a dressed heirloom turkey in the fifteen- to twenty-five-pound range than those for whom the challenge has been to just get a store-bought bird wrestled into and out of the shopping cart. The point from which to begin exploring this market would indeed be twelve to fifteen poults, perhaps just five each of a number of varieties bought from a noted source. Varieties should always be trialed in the real world of your farm or smallholding or markets before making any investments in quality seedstock.

Heirloom poults will cost nine to fifteen dollars each when bought in small, as-hatched lots. Most sources will ship them in lots of no less than twelve to fifteen poults for warmth and safety in transit. Many will offer the option to buy as few as five of a certain variety, but orders must total ten to fifteen youngsters. Such poults, if well tended, should reach a handy market weight at around twenty-six to twenty-eight weeks of age. Poults for fall harvest, the holiday season, are typically started from mid-April to mid-May. They can leave the early, more-sheltered brooder/grower unit at ten to twelve weeks of age and be moved to a range-growing situation. It is here that many producers actually find tending the birds to be the most taxing. The heirloom birds will fly up as they mature, especially the females. They are served well by that vigor and alertness on the range, but they will require more from the producer than cursory inspections from the seat of a four-wheeler. Many, for example, have found that shelters carefully constructed for range birds keep producers especially busy as they have to go out each evening, catch the birds off of the roofline, and shut them inside the house. On range these birds can be quite vulnerable to predation, and there are some varmints here in Missouri that like turkey legs even more than my little sister. The birds should be shut into their sleeping quarters every night and let out again every morning. Plucking twenty-pound birds from roosting places head high and higher will quench the ardor of even the most passionate of beginning turkey keepers.

With any number of ranging birds, investing in a guard dog accustomed to ranging poultry is quite justifiable. A good guard dog will even challenge and repel aerial predators. Turkeys aren't cows and require frequent, close observation and producer attention when on range.

Housing requirements for a mature turkey are six to eight square feet (roughly the same as is alloted for a finishing hog in a confinement unit). Each bird will need ten to fifteen inches of roost space (many will not provide roosts for breeding turkeys to prevent foot and leg injuries caused to the birds when coming down from the roost), and they will each need a minimum of six inches of feed trough space. The traditional stocking rate for turkeys on range has been four hundred birds per acre, and that parcel would be turned to other uses for three to four years to disrupt any disease and parasite cycles.

Turkeys aren't grazers; they, like chickens, are omnivores, though seeds and grains make up the majority of their diet. There is much archaeological evidence that turkeys are among those rare creatures that may have largely domesticated themselves. From the wild they drew ever closer to humans for the spilt grains, food wastes, and added safety from other predators.

On range, growing and breeding turkeys must still be kept on full feeds of appropriate, complete rations to achieve desired levels of growth or reproductive performance. The real benefits that accrue to a bird on range are the stimulus of a changing environment, an ever-freshened environment, exposure to sunshine, improved feather quality, the addition of numerous items in small amounts to the diet, and the exercise that improves muscle tone and thus the table qualities of the bird.

One thing that has greatly improved since my first turkey venture is the quality, variety, and availability of turkey rations. There are now starter, grower, and breeder rations available from many of the major feed companies. Some even have one-bag formulations that will work for birds at several stages of development. These feeds now exist in the proper formulations to foster rapid and efficient growth while preventing the development of nutritionally related conditions, such as leg problems or angel wing (misshapen wings caused improper protein intake).

Small lots of growing birds and small breeding groups are probably best and most easily fed with commercially available complete feeds. Pelleted rations, though one of the costliest forms of feed processing, can reduce some feed wastage with older birds, as spilt pellets can be gleaned by the birds from where they fall. The pelleting process can also release more of the nutrient content of the feedstuffs. Buying feedstuffs in small lots, as needed every couple of weeks, is one of the proven ways to average out high and low feed costs over the course of a year.

Some feed companies also offer a poultry concentrate that can be blended with locally produced grains to formulate rations that can be prepared on the home farm. This would be a measure perhaps best pursued with grower and breeder rations that are much less complex and require fewer ingredients. Also, the old rule of thumb is that to justify an investment in on-farm feed processing equipments you need to be producing at least one hundred tons of feed yearly. Such equipment can be used to produce rations for many different species, however.

Due to the very small amounts consumed daily by very young birds, starter rations are probably best bought as commercial, complete feeds sold in a crumble form. In the earliest days these feeds will be consumed only in fractions of an ounce by each bird. Processing the crumbles and later the mini-pellets assures that such rations have the bite-after-bite consistency needed by these small yet rapidly growing birds.

Before the development of modern rations, poultry species were ranged to allow them access to a number of different potential nutrient resources. Turkeys aren't grazers like geese, but on range they do benefit from contact with clean soil and fresh air. They should range on fine-stemmed and leafed plant varieties to prevent crop binding from plant ingestion. The classic plant variety for poultry ranges was fine-bladed bluegrass.

Although in the wild state turkeys do range about a fair-sized territory, they are doing so primarily in search of mast varieties and generally in small, kindred groups. They can be equally stifled on an overcrowded range or lot as in a confinement building

The spin placed on heirloom turkeys and their meat output at the moment is their comparative rarity and the more "natural" methods and systems being used to produce them. There is another possible marketing point that producers should employ: To consumers heirloom turkeys will not look like the Broadbreasted White birds that so dominate the marketplace now. They will look different both in the display case in the store and on the serving platter at home.

In poultry production circles now, white-feathered birds—whether turkeys, waterfowl, or chickens—meet substantial buyer resistance. This is, I believe, because of the bad experiences so many have had with factory-farmed white-feathered birds. Some have also blamed their aversion on the fact that white-feathered birds are so easily targeted by predators when on range. However, most predators strike on the basis of need and opportunity and with no expressed color preference of which I am aware.

Some branding in the marketplace might even be possible with some of the heritage turkey varieties, as has been done with Black Angus or Hereford beef. A flock of good Bourbon Red or Royal Palm turkeys are eye-catching road pasture poultry. A neighbor keeps a small flock of young Bourbon Red toms in a poultry yard alongside a well-traveled county road. Strutting with tails fanned, they draw many to stop and inquire if there are birds for sale, and to buy other items from the roadside stand that those folks operate. They are a vivid, feathered example of what the folks on Madison Avenue call an "AGM": attention-getting mechanism.

Excepting a few high-profile examples to the contrary, meat turkey production is not going to become a high-volume venture for most family farm— and smallholding-based producers. They will emerge for most as a short or sideline enterprise to be coupled with other closely aligned ventures such as broiler or egg production. With ten-dollar-plus poult costs, six months or more production time, and substantial food and labor costs, this is not an inexpensive meat bird to produce.

For most of the consuming public, turkeys are seen as a select bird to produce and to purchase, one that is perhaps best targeted for certain high-profile meals that fall late in each year. These birds are generally sold one at a time to families and will not be turned into slices and nuggets consumed the year around. Consumers are willing to pay that special heirloom price for a bird to be eaten at one or two big family meals each year.

There is a growing role for those wanting to move beyond what is essentially the operation of a small heirloom turkey feedyard. They are taking up a breed, improving it through selective breeding, and hatching and rearing these birds to create some marketing opportunities throughout the course of an entire year. By offering select-bred poults, hatching eggs, some seedstock, and modest numbers of meat birds, a venture could be created that may be supplied from one, two, or three trios of one or two of the heirloom varieties.

The size to which an heirloom turkey venture can grow will vary from farm to farm and producer to producer. It should be grown only to the level that will enable the producer to be fully and fairly compensated for his or her good efforts, whether that means a yearly output of fifty, one hundred fifty, or even five hundred birds. And it will succeed because when that type of committed producer talks turkey, others know to listen to and believe him.

When marketing poultry from a rural base, as with most livestock, you have to present your birds as the "go-to" flock and yourself as one of the "go-to" producers.

Most people have eaten turkey; it's now in so many different products such as hotdogs and luncheon meats that we probably eat more of it than we think. The heirloom stock is being marketed primarily as whole birds, some even on foot, and not every consumer now has the skills and confidence needed to get maximum use from a food item of such size and cost. Many aren't sure what actually makes an heirloom, and many more don't know what to fully make of one when they have it.

The Royal Palm and Bourbon Red are the most popular varieties in our area now, but there are an increasing number of inquiries about both Buff and Lilac varieties. Something new or different will nearly always draw added attention in the short term, but it is the presence of dependable and respected breeders that assures a breed's success and survival in an area. The Lilac, like the Slate, is one of the most challenging varieties with which to work and, like the Slate, will hatch in three different hues

Slate is a grayish appearance, sometimes referred to as "blue" in poultry circles. Slate poults can thus hatch true to color, Black, or in a faded Splash pattern. Breeding Slate to Slate, both of good color, will result in 50 percent with Slate coloring, 25 percent Black, and 25 percent with miscoloring. The Black and Splash mated together will produce all Slate-colored birds. Slate to Black will produce 50 percent of each, and Splash to Splash will tend to further dilute the color.

Variety choice can be a very subjective matter, but on the smallholding and especially in the early years producers should key in on just one variety. The producer should take the time to learn the ins and outs of one breed before moving on to another, and be a student of that breed before buying into it. The best approach to variety selection, I believe, would be to trim the potential varietal list to two or three and then acquire ten to twelve poults of each variety. They can then be grown out on the home farm or smallholding and their performance there carefully evaluated.

Early marketing with small lots can give the producer a feel for what the available markets want and will support without the pressure of having a great many birds to move within a short window of opportunity. In the direct marketing process much valuable information can flow from consumer to producer if he or she is open to receiving it. Desired market weights, favored varieties, preferences for toms or hens (hopefully they will balance out), and more should emerge fairly quickly.

What happened with my first turkey venture befalls literally hundreds of others each year. At the local feed store the other day a warehouseman was bemoaning the gift of one of those globs of turkey meat still in the feathers. He had been given a Broadbreasted Bronze tom that dressed out at thirty-three pounds, and his family finally had to give up on the Thanksgiving turkey that wouldn't go away.

Heirloom turkeys make sense on the small farm for economic reasons, also. They are easier keepers, grow out to more practical harvest weights, should be easier to lift and crate, and will perform well in simpler housing. They are going to eat and consume feedstuffs in relation to their size; however, skimped-on or poor-quality rations will cause health and structural problems and will extend the period of time a bird will be on the farm and on feed. Likewise, poor-quality genetics will impact time and costs to produce along with the selling price.

I don't want this to sound like I am bashing turkey keeping, but what became apparent to us quite early on was that there is often a mighty big gap between how many turkeys you can produce and how many turkeys you can produce for a real profit. Growth and expansion with these alternative poultry ventures lie not in building numbers but in building quality and an identity as one who knows and supplies quality birds for the table or as seedstock. And as one who will share his expertise.

Typically, turkey poults are sold as-hatched. Borrowing the well-documented ratio common to chickens, you should expect six young toms for every four young hens bought or hatched. In a very small lot it is possible that the ratio will skew badly toward one gender or the other. From a shipment of twelve or fifteen poults it would be wise to expect to raise no more than one trio of some promise and one or two backup birds of keeper quality. And it is insurance of the wisest type to always hold back a second, backup tom. Entire breeding years have been lost when the single male held back was killed by predators or proved infertile.

These large heirloom varieties aren't nearly as widely available as many chicken and waterfowl varieties. Some hatcheries still offer only Broad-breasted White and Bronze varieties, and these may come from a relative handful of sources. Others may just offer two or three of the heritage varieties, and where these are produced in volume concerns as to quality and genetic purity often ensue. With a variety decided on many will buy stock from two or three clearly distinct sources to have a broader genetic base from which to begin building a flock. They may begin by breeding true to those two or three lines. They will then combine birds to create a new line bred to the demands of that farm or holding and the needs of those markets being served.

An adult trio, especially one bought early in the breeding year, will easily cost $150.00 to $250.00 or more. A good started trio in the fall will typically bring $75.00 to $125.00 and then have to be wintered on a growing/developing ration.

Turkeys aren't spectacular egg layers, and yes, you can eat a turkey egg. Such eggs, however, are more valuable for the poults that can hatch from them. Nearly every spring we get a call from someone who has caught a couple of wild turkey poults or found a nest of eggs and asks about having them incubated. These are clear violations of wildlife codes and can subject you to severe legal consequences. And wildlife officers can fairly easily spot birds in even the largest of flocks of like-colored birds.

In a mild winter some turkey hens may begin to lay as early as February here in the Midwest. We have also had turkey hens continue laying into the month of September in unlit housing. Shorter days and cooler and damper weather can be a real challenge to later-hatched birds in simple housing.

As noted earlier there is something of a seasonal aspect to turkey marketing, and it coincides with the seasonal aspects of their natural reproductive cycle when not manipulated by supplemental lighting, heat, and feeding. Expect sixty to ninety eggs per hen, with most of the egg laying occurring in March, April, and May. In most small flock situations you will probably get more eggs than you need hatchlings, but reproductive performance should never be neglected in the selective breeding process.

A turkey egg takes twenty-eight days to hatch. We have incubated both chicken and turkey eggs in the same cabinet incubator at the same time with good results. It does take careful record keeping when managing the two different eggs in the same unit, but neither eggs nor hatchlings are easily confused for each other.

With small breeding pens, modest numbers of eggs will generally go into the incubator each week. The fresher the egg going into the incubator, the greater its likelihood of hatchability. The preferred norm is no more than seven days from laying, though that figure can be pushed to ten to twelve days with reduced expectations of hatching rate.

With small numbers and very rare varieties, every egg matters. They can be stored prior to incubation in an appropriate-sized egg carton or flat rack. It is best to store eggs for incubation in air temperatures of between forty-five and sixty degrees Fahrenheit. Store them small-end down and raise one side of the carton by elevating it on an empty carton or brick. Each time you pass by turn the carton to elevate the other end to prevent the air cells from sticking in the egg. Storing eggs in a very warm place can cause a state called pre-incubation that can affect hatching time and rate. Do not save for incubation any badly soiled or stained eggs. Dirty spots should be cleaned by scarping with a knife blade or light rubbing with fine steel wool or sandpaper. Eggs should be candled before being placed in the incubator to find and discard any with fine cracks. Do not set poorly formed eggs or eggs with surface abnormalities.

In an incubator many will dedicate a tray or rack to turkey eggs. An extra-large egg rack, suitable for turkey eggs, can be bought for ten dollars or less. With light pencil markings denote things like laying date, breeding pen data, hatching date, and the like. These should be backed up with an incubator log that includes all of this and a diary for the hatching year.

For the first few days after hatching we will brood a few young poults with baby chicks. They will rather quickly outgrow their chicken brooder mates and must be moved to a brooder of their own within a few days. There is concern about chickens and turkeys having close contact due to the communicable nature of the disease blackhead, which can afflict turkeys. It can happen, but I believe the real factors are intense crowding, stress, and keeping the birds in large numbers.

We use a starter feed blended for the needs of young large fowl, including heavy breed chickens, young waterfowl, and turkey poults. It is not a cheap feed, but fast-growing young fowl can develop a number of structural problems if not fed well-formulated rations.

Brooding turkeys will require careful management beginning with the size and height of the brooder box or unit in which they are to be contained. We use a wooden, box-type brooder to block drafts and provide better protection from vermin. This first brooder is thirty inches by sixty inches and the solid sides are thirty inches high. It is heated with a 125- or 250-watt heat bulb in a simple reflector suspended above the unit. Heat levels can be regulated by raising or lowering the heat lamp or reducing bulb size. In very warm weather we will use a clear, hundred-watt bulb to encourage the poults to eat and drink around the clock. A red-tinted bulb will help to counter problems with feather picking.

A square foot of brooder space should be provided for each poult. After feathering we move them to an outside brooder fronted with a roofed sunporch. The birds can walk out on the elevated sunporch in fair weather, waste falls through the mesh-bottomed run or porch, and on cold days a heat lamp reflector with appropriate-sized bulb can be placed in the enclosed sleeping area.

A clear hundred-watt bulb in a reflector can provide a lot of warmth, but such bulbs may soon become difficult to acquire. Do not use the soft light bulbs as they produce little warmth, and the safety bulbs can cause poisoning if the birds ever pick at broken fragments of such bulbs. Early and later hatched birds may also benefit from the added presence of a reptile tank light in the brooder. These provide beneficial light with the same wavelengths as sunshine.

There is a lot of misinformation going around that young turkeys hatch dumb and then get dumber. The truth is that they are the descendants of a game bird considered one of the wiliest creatures on the North American continent.

As they come out of the hatcher the poults should be inspected for problems like umbilical ill, and poults with pronounced problems should be humanely euthanized. As they are placed into the brooder, dip their bills into the waterer a time or two and then into the feedstuffs while their bills are still wet so bits of feed will cling to them.

Early poult care can be facilitated with the following measures:

1. Feeders and waterers should be positioned to give the young birds easy access to their contents, though not right under the brooder heat source. Avoid waterers with very large lips to prevent the drowning of young and inexperienced birds.

2. Marbles can be cleansed and placed in the waterer lips to reduce drowning potential. In an earlier time small stones were used for this purpose. Colorful marbles placed in waterers and feeders will induce the young birds to pick at their contents and increase consumption.

3. Red-based feeders and waterers will also draw the young birds to them and their contents.

4. Slightly warm the first water for the young birds. Add about a teaspoon of white sugar to every pint of drinking water for the first couple of days to give the youngsters an extra energy boost. This can be especially beneficial to hatchlings that have had a rough trip through the mails.
5. A couple of times each week add a good vitamin/electrolyte product to the drinking water to give a further boost to the rapidly growing youngsters.

As the birds head into what could be likened to their teenage life stage, feed consumption will take a real jump. It can be a painful time when you are writing out all of those checks to the feedstore, but feed is their fuel for the important jobs of growth and carcass development. Continue them on a good starter/grower or grower ration, and remember that you cannot starve a profit out of a bird.

As things currently stand, two or three trios of one or two different turkey varieties is going to form the base for most heritage turkey ventures. Yes, the factory farmers turn them out by the tens of thousands, but, a few tales to the contrary, epicurean turkeys leave two-lane blacktop country just a few birds at a time.

There are two marketing seasons a year for heirloom turkeys. In the first half of the year there will be the greatest demand for breeding birds, hatching eggs, and poults. In the first few warm days in late winter or early spring the demand begins for breeding birds, especially those going into their first or second year of production. Such birds will be costly as the producer has borne the feed and facility costs to bring them into the new breeding year.

At our last farmers' market of the season last year one breeder arrived with several young trios of Royal Palms. They were priced very reasonably, but I overheard a conversation between the breeder and one potential customer. Both were eyeing the graying November skies above them. The would-be buyer asked if the breeder would be back in the spring with breeding stock. He was told yes, but that prices would then be double on young toms and triple on young hens. The lesson was offered, and I hope that it was learned.

In the early warm days of spring other buyers are out and about looking for birds for a seasonal backyard project, a turkey breeding venture of their own, and to grow out for sale in simpler, seasonal housing facilities and systems. Those not wanting the task of taking birds through a winter season will pay higher prices for turkey stock early in the year.

The second season for heritage turkey sales generally comes in the late fall. They are a premium product targeted for the special holiday meals that come late in the year. Consumers generally make room in the budget for special food items that will highlight the large family meals of that season. Come September and October real bargains can be found in the form of later-hatched poults and older breeding birds. It's a good time to shop if you're equipped to winter them. One fall we set up a newly acquired trio of young Royal Palms in a simple lean-to addition to an outbuilding. It was enclosed with used sheet metal, and half of the south-facing wall was covered with just wire mesh to admit fresh air and sunshine. They winter well with a bit of straw litter on the floor. Another good time to buy breeding stock may come in late spring or early summer when hatcheries and others are breaking up their breeding flocks. The birds will have to be wintered over but often can be bought at very reduced prices. Last year a friend was offered 125 birds of six different varieties when one hatchery breeder ceased production for the year in the presence of a summer drought.

We do not pen adult turkeys and chickens together here. We work hard to keep their pens a minimum of eight feet apart, a distance believed to be sufficient to prevent the aerosol spread of disease organisms. Nor do we immediately move different species into pens once they have been evacuated. We throw a lot of lime onto yards and in houses, remove litter and manure, and try for rest times of thirty or more days between pen uses when changing species. Still, the idea of a mixed-species poultry yard can be a hot button issue for many, but I maintain that overcrowding and poor placement leads to the greatest number of health problems in the poultry yard. A well-run poultry yard is like a well-run farm shop: everything has its place, it is kept contained there, and each zone is well and carefully maintained.

I quickly learned it is more satisfactory and more profitable to keep modest numbers of those birds that please me and my customers than to try to turn our smallholding into an ark for the whole of the poultry kingdom. This poultry renaissance of ours is driven by very small, micro-, and backyard-level producers, and that means closely fitting together poultry ventures. They are often stacked in an orderly and noncompetitive fashion on quite small parcels of land. Rare breeds have had to be closely contained to protect their limited numbers; pedigreed matings require tight penning. Careful containment is the only way to maintain breed integrity. Safety is also an issue for containment. Birds must be fenced in and predators out, and in many parts of this nation poultry species are going to have to be closely contained for several winter months each year. Some of the enduring areas of poultry production are located where containment is a must: the upper Midwest, upstate New York, eastern Pennsylvania, and northern Missouri.

I have seen poultry yards that have been in continuous use for many years, decades even, with continuing good results. They are carefully managed, the birds going into them have been ruthlessly culled, and the greatest emphasis in the selection process is placed on growth, vigor, and durability. Good management makes the poultry flocks other, enduring parts of the biota that is a successfully run farm or smallholding. To better facilitate the care and operation of poultry lots and yards, some or all of the following may be in order for your place on the land:

1. The outside poultry run should slope away from the house in a gentle manner. On such strips of land the rainfall or melt will quickly run away from the house and the birds contained there. Position a strip of sod some yards wide at the end of the runs, and the runoff will be naturally filtered as it passes through the sodded area.

2. To begin a good lot lay down a layer of two to four inches of clean sand. Firmly tamp it down.

3. Over the sand place a packed, two-inch layer of cull ag lime.

4. Check the lot often for low places and scratched-out potholes. Fill them quickly with hard-packed lime to prevent water from pooling there.

5. Rain will remove much of the waste from the lot surface, and it will then be screened by passing through the sod strip below the lot.

6. Give the lot a heavy dusting of fresh lime a couple of times each year. Scoop up badly soiled or deteriorating areas and rebuild them from the base up.

7. In England, where smallholding space is really at a limit, many now use shredded rubber from old tires to surface their side-yard and garden-based poultry yards. It is environmentally sound, easily cleaned, and prevents problems with mud and dampness in their wet climate.

Long, narrow lots will discourage attacks from winged predators, as will stringing heavy-gauge wire across the top of the pen in a zigzag pattern. Long strips of silver Mylar material tacked to poles around the poultry yard will whip in the wind and also deter flying predators. A nighttime predator, such as an owl, will not fly through a strobe light, if you can find one at the yard sale of a disco-loving neighbor. As large a bird as a turkey may be, it should always be shut securely into place at nightfall.

In the Missouri township where I grew up I can remember day-ranging flocks of between two thousand and three thousand young Bronze turkeys. There were also breeding flocks of three hundred to five hundred adult birds. The meat birds were transported live to processors on trucks with coop-like dividers. The breeders produced eggs that were hatched on the farm and were sold across a wide area to other high-volume turkey feeders.

That era is past and will, I suspect, never return. Turkey and chicken meat did much to establish the current cheap food policies in this country. They are now used in nearly countless forms as prepared and fast food items, and that market demands fast, cheaply produced birds the year around. The confined flock will be one of the last factory farm ventures to be dislodged, if it ever really will be.

There never really was a place for the small, artisanal farmer in mass marketing. It is a wholesale market with the only premium in place being for production in volume. The small flock turkey folks are going to be men and women apart, doing everything from breeding up future generations of stock to scooping up manure to taking their production directly into the marketplace and right up to the consumer.

As I write this there are just two independent processors of poultry in Missouri. They are primarily set up for broiler chickens, cannot really handle birds in any number, and one of the two is quite elderly. There is a distance of several hundred miles for even some Missouri producers to travel to reach them, and the producers are still left with the task of storage and transport until they can be sold.

There is a road to the future in the production of heritage-based turkeys, but it will probably be a long, winding, and most colorful one. And the producer will have to be in the driver's seat from the front gate of the farm to the consumer's doorstep, whether the consumer is buying hatching eggs, poults, or meat birds.

The heritage turkey says "Americana" and "real local food" as do few other food items. The varieties are often reflective of specific geographical regions of the nation; the Narragansett to the Northeast and the Bourbon Red to the South. The heirloom producer can play this trump card to the maximum by breeding and raising his own birds to be directly marketed from the farm or smallholding.

Thirty years ago, long before the poultry renaissance and the rise of interest in heirloom poultry, I visited a Missouri farm where numerous turkey varieties were being kept in small breeding groups. These folks were placing breeding trios of several different varieties of turkey into eight-by-sixteen-foot hog range houses. The houses were divided in half with a short segment of a fifty-four-inch-high cattle panel, and each half of the divided house sheltered a breeding trio. Seven other sixteen-feet-long-by-fifty-four-inch-high cattle panels were used to create two large pens fronting outward from the southern-facing houses. The pens and shelters had a deep straw litter, a practice old-timers will recall as straw yarding.

This family kept four varieties of turkey with between one and three trios (one tom and two hens) of each of those varieties. A few extra birds were kept on hand in case of injury or death loss among the primary breeding birds. From their modest numbers and simple facilities they produced for sale poults, hatching eggs, breeding stock, and some birds for the table. Their housing and fencing materials were bought used, and their main investment in equipment was for a cabinet incubator with a 240-egg capacity.

A friend with a small flock of a rather rare turkey variety has found his niche with a turkey known for its vivid coloring, the Lilac. The poults do not color up all the same, but that challenge is just one of the elements of their appeal to him. Most of his sales are of small lots of young birds to others who want to grow out a few birds for their own use or just have a few turkeys around the farmyard. Such buyers are drawn to the unusual color of his birds, and in explaining their breeding and care my friend establishes his bonafides as a reliable turkey supplier whose birds are worth a premium.

A breeding trio with two well-bred hens can produce a substantial number of eggs during a laying season that can begin in early spring and continue into late summer. They won't lay like Leghorn hens, but a single trio may be all that is needed to fill the local demand for a particular turkey variety. Overproduction can undo many local niche markets; alternative poultry ventures should never be grown to the point where they skew the farm too far in the direction of a single type of production. An awful lot of birds over the years have been lost to "too many turkeys" disease.

We have had our best results with heirloom turkeys—highest fertility and hatchability—when keeping them penned just as pairs or trios with a single male in each pen. With some of the lighter weight breeds you might stretch that to three or four hens per tom, but the wisest choice would be to just go ahead and establish a second breeding trio in another pen.

A few other lessons I have been taught by veteran turkey producers and the birds themselves:

1. Multiple toms in a pen will pester each other and interfere with mating activity. They will increase the stress level on the hens, and fertility will suffer.

2. For higher fertility and to reduce wear on the hens, we try to use first-year toms in the breeding pen. They are smaller and more agile. With some matings we have used two-year-old and even older toms, but do watch closely that they have not become too large and cumbersome or too wearing on the hens.

3. We generally turn the hens after two seasons in the breeding pens, but allowances are made for rarer and better performing birds.

4. Remove from the breeding pen any female showing excessive feather wear, damage to the back, or injury stemming from mating activity. Canvas saddles have been used to protect some turkey hens from the wear and potential breeding injury associated with mating activity.

5. Breeding birds must be monitored closely for condition and fed a well-formulated ration to keep them hale and productive.

6. Nest boxes are generally eighteen to twenty-four inches square, with sides six- to eight-inches high, and placed at floor level in the house. We have used old truck tires filled with straw for turkey nests, also.

In evaluating young birds to be retained for breeding stock, become familiar with the variety standards of type set down by the American Poultry Association in its book *The American Standard of Perfection*. This is a volume that should be owned by all who are serious about breeding better-performing birds. Beyond type, the turkey producer should also be selecting for optimal growth and feed efficiency. Growth and hardiness, I believe, are indicative of birds with bred-in body capacity, health, and that hard-to-define will to live and thrive.

In selecting from the larger, faster-growing birds in each hatch group, you are selecting for ever more natural performance and vigor. The longer a line is in place on the farm, the greater the level of natural immunity to the "bug" problem that is a part of every farm with livestock.

An adult tom turkey with tail spread and in full strut is one of the most impressive creatures in the farmyard. He is a walking, gobbling advertisement for a most traditional form of agriculture. I will never forget the look on my great-nephew's face as he was playing near a pen of turkeys and heard a tom issue a deep "putt" call for the first time. He felt it as much as heard it and a look of comprehension of something deep within him shone in his eyes. For several days after that he didn't want my wife, Phyllis, to put any eggs in the icebox as they might be "hatch" eggs.

Think how often pictures of tom turkeys have made it into news stories about farm matters and are used in advertising. The turkey and the little red hen are even staples of children's literature.

That identifiability and appeal can be built on in promoting the heirloom turkey varieties. A warm feeling can accompany acquiring some of such stock, but that warm regard will continue only as long as there are dependable producers in place and concerned with the integrity of the birds. The factory-farmed turkey is backed by a seven-day hotline leading up to the Thanksgiving holiday. The successful small flock producer is on the line 24/7/365—breeding, growing, promoting, and marketing the better bird.

CHAPTER 3

Waterfowl
Ducks, Geese, and Swan

MUSCOVY DUCK

Back in the mid-seventies I was a field representative for the Hubbard Milling Company. As one of old Mother Hubbard's minions, a part of my assigned territory was an old-order Amish community. Those folks were pretty good stock farmers, embracing livestock keeping of all types and at all levels. It was on one of those farms that I saw two of the largest flocks of waterfowl I've ever encountered. The farmer kept flocks of several hundred White Pekin ducks and Emden geese to produce hatching eggs for the now long-gone Heart of Missouri hatchery.

Amish farms are home to many hatchery breeding flocks even today, and the Amish community has never lost the appreciation for what a poultry flock can do in creating a more fully diversified farm with greater environmental and economic integrity. Those two flocks of waterfowl were kept on large hillside lots rising up from the farmyard. They were sheltered in open-sided range shelters originally used for hogs and fed in old self-feeders, also once used for swine production. It was a large feed account for that era, and those birds went through several tons of feed each week.

In most instances these days waterfowl are kept in very small numbers, have become little more than a novelty fowl for many, and breed preservation work has fallen to but a couple of hatcheries and a modest number of exhibition breeders. Rising grain and supplement costs have raised real concerns about the survival of some waterfowl breeds, as many of the breeds are quite large.

The best-selling ducks at our local market are the colorful varieties, preferably with "green heads," that will look pretty on the "lake" that most rurban folks think a necessity for their farmettes. Next in demand appear to be the Muscovies and the bantam ducks, the Calls and West Indies.

Around Easter each year a few ducklings and goslings arrive at local farm supply stores, where their arrival and resultant purchases are met with all sorts of myths and misinformation. A lot of little ducks and geese get bought by ones and twos, are taken home and dropped into icy cold March and April pond water, and wind up as turtle food before the next sunrise. Of all of the poultry species, ducks and geese are the most hardy and long-lived—after they are grown out and well-feathered, that is.

Waterfowl production has been a big business in the past. Duck figures prominently in many forms of cuisine, especially Asian cooking, and roast goose is perceived as very elite fare with a great many historical roots.

Geese were once prized for their vocal nature as feathered watchdogs, and there are numerous accounts of them warning of raiders, both animal and human. Geese were once kept for their down for featherbed and pillow fill as well. My grandparents especially prized their down pillows and bedding on cold winter nights in our old, two-story farmhouse.

Geese have also been used to weed growing crops from wine grapes to strawberries to cotton. In fact, the quest for old-time Cotton Patch goose genetics has been one of the classic stories in the annals of poultry breed preservation work. They are the fowl variety that comes the closest to being a full-time creature of meadow and lea. Once started they can meet many of their nutrient needs on a good pasture such as bluegrass, but they will need grain and winter shelter as the seasons turn.

Some years ago I was loading out hay on an eastern Missouri farm that was home to a small flock of Pomeranian geese that had largely tended themselves for over a decade. At night they bedded down in a lean-to off the main barn, they worked the barnyard for spilt grain and feed wastes, went out onto the adjacent pastures each day with the cow herd, and had access to a small pond. A few new goslings were hatched every year or two, and the little flock ambled through the seasons as a fixture of that particular barnyard. Certainly, they were given some extra care and feeding in the cold times, but they were as true a low-input venture as I have ever seen.

Our Amish client was in the waterfowl business on a major scale. For most folks, however, the marketing niche they will find is apt to be quite small.

For a time, a friend in eastern Pennsylvania grew out two hundred White Pekin ducklings at a time for sale to the restaurant trade. He converted a small modular farrowing house into a facility with about four hundred square feet of mesh flooring over a small, self-contained pit. The young ducks could be brooded and grown out there, the wastes were used for fertilizer, and he sold three to four sets of young ducks each year. They were not a big venture, but they were converting to checks that certainly evened out the cash flow.

A young duck has a dressed weight of around four pounds, and the heavy breed ducks will reach this weight by twelve to sixteen weeks of age. Numerous hatcheries offer lines of White Pekin ducks that have long been selectively bred for rapid growth and high dressing yield, and crosses of Pekins and Muscovies are also channeled into the market for duck meat. There does seem to be something of a seasonal aspect to waterfowl on the table in the United States, with the rich nature of the meat lending itself more to the cool and cold seasons as game meat does.

Most people who have partaken of goose or duck recently have probably consumed wild birds harvested during the autumn and winter shooting seasons. This can be good or bad depending on how the birds have been handled afield, but a bad experience should not deter someone from trying a true, farm-fresh, young goose or duck. In most instances they are a very big bird on the platter, are not the easiest of fowl to dress, they present with a dark rich meat, and most people have eaten them roasted or in elaborate cooking methods. There are far more ways to prepare a duck than a l'orange or with a plum sauce, and roast goose, though a classic, is actually a rather simple preparation.

And then there is that whole foie gras thing. Foie gras is a pâté made from fatted duck liver. It was traditionally produced by force-feeding ducks a wet, high-concentrate ration and by keeping the birds in closely confined cooping. The goal is to produce an enlarged and higher yielding liver of desirable taste and texture. Foie gras is a food item that has been around for a very long time and is quite pricey. It has always been produced in limited amounts and from limited outlets and is one product that the animal rights activists have not won a total victory against. It is offered less often in the restaurant trade here, though not abroad, and the image of pâté de fois gras continues to add to the allure of waterfowl on the table.

A friend who has taken up duck egg production on his small truck farm is working on an alternative foie gras. It will be a slow process, and he is beginning by breeding up a line of White Pekin ducks of exceptional size to produce more meat, larger eggs, and naturally larger livers. At the same time he is trialing several different ration formulations and adding water to them to further boost consumption levels, though not by force-feeding. He is seeking to naturally produce a waterfowl liver pâté product that will approximate foie gras of the grand style. It will not be a project of short duration, but it is a worthy challenge and should he succeed. . . . Well, he lives near several major cities, has experience direct marketing poultry meat items, and he just could emerge with a good alternative that is less costly to produce. And using duck fat in several different forms of food preparation and recipes is certainly growing in popularity right now.

Many chefs render their own duck fat as a by-product of cooking duck in many of the traditional recipes associated with it. In the cooking shows current now you can watch chefs spooning it out carefully and treating duck fat like so much liquid gold. It is not likely that a market will ever develop for fat-type ducks like it did for lard-type hogs, but it does show that something new can emerge from even the most traditional and that producers should always be open and welcoming to new uses for their production.

A waterfowl venture is most apt to be an outgrowth from an already existing poultry venture on the family farm or smallholding. Sales of waterfowl are generally as meat birds in small lots or for a few birds to other small-scale producers. Duck and goose eggs are edible, though a three-egg omelet made from them will fill a mighty big plate. Some have reported issues with flavor and texture, and waterfowl eggs are a bit more viscous. Many report liking that added bit of texture. A lot of egg eating quality hinges upon how the eggs are handled and stored, and some ducks are awfully haphazard in their laying habits. Ducks will sometimes lay wherever the whim hits, but where eggs are being gathered yards and nests should be well strawed, the eggs gathered several times each day, and the yards walked often for any signs of stolen out nest. If there is any doubt as to time of lay or the eggs are badly stained, they should simply be discarded.

Duck eggs are also used to produce *balut* and century eggs, highly valued by some folks of Asian ancestry. *Balut* is prepared by boiling a partially incubated egg and then eating the yolk and duck embryo in its shell. Century eggs are preserved in a saline solution for a period of several weeks to several months during which the yolks turn black, and they are among the black food items highly valued by certain cultures. A friend living near the large university town of Columbia, Missouri, fielded many questions about such eggs from foreign students and university staff. Sanitary issues were such that he did not pursue this market despite its apparent lucrative potential. In a similar vein, a few years back, I received a phone call from a lady with Eastern European roots who was looking for fresh duck blood to add to a variety of soups and sausage products. The small producer has to be open to all potential sales, but some may require such special measures as to be beyond the abilities and systems available to a small-scale Cayuga producer.

Duck eggs are finding their way into stores in Great Britain and Europe. Their larger size will require special cartons and handling, and the chosen packaging for duck eggs there seems to be for lots of four or six eggs. And all duck eggs do not look the same. Breeds like the Khaki Campbell and Runner will produce large white eggs and in quite substantial numbers.

Other breeds will produce eggs with a slight bluish cast. And then there is the Cayuga, the black duck with the cartoon-colored eggs.

Some of the eggs of the Cayuga when they first begin the laying cycle will be nearly black. They will then lighten to a dark green color, reminiscent of emu eggs. Samantha Wiseman, a farming colleague, uses Cayuga ducks as natural pest control among many of her fruit and produce crops. When she found a small market for some of their dark-shelled eggs in the farmers' markets in the St. Louis area, it was a pleasant surprise. Cayuga eggs have become a bit of a signature product for her, and all poultry producers should realize that once an egg is put to use in cooking or baking the eggshell is left behind and quickly discarded.

Primary sales of waterfowl in our area have been for small lots of ducks as ornamentals or small lots of ducks or geese (preferably hatchlings or young breeders) with which to launch a new small waterfowl venture. Consumers appear to want birds in lots of less than eight to ten, the normal minimum for shipment through the mail. The buyers also seem willing to pay a premium for birds that are old enough to be easily sexed, that are of the more rare or colorful varieties, that are started and no longer need the time-consuming early care, and that are offered by knowledgeable and personable breeders that can and will answer their questions about the care and breeding of the birds.

I once stood in a farm supply store chewing hard on the inside of my cheek as an inexperienced store clerk sold some pricey little Easter ducklings to some inexperienced folks with young children. He assured them that he could sex the ducklings based solely on the size of their feet and that the downy ducklings would thrive in their still icy pond.

Little ducks will plunge fearlessly into water, but often with most disastrous results. Unless being reared with an adult female that has gone through the brooding process the ducklings' down lacks the natural oils to keep them insulated and safe from chilling. The little guys receive those oils by preening through the feathers of the breast of their brood mother. Oil glands there produce the natural secretions needed to keep the ducklings protected when swimming.

The return to the farming world of the concepts of sustainability and increased diversification mean that a role for waterfowl production on at least a modest scale is emerging again. Emerging, but far from fully back and securely in place. Flocks of ten, fifteen, or maybe twenty-five birds or a bit more have a role to play, and even a pair or a trio of such birds can produce some meaningful sales. A couple of years back my friend Neal Gray of Alabama bought a trio of Ancona ducks. He lost one of the young hens before the first breeding season but in the first year sold $150 worth of ducklings produced by the remaining pair. The Ancona breed was not common in his area, and when offered in small lots they quickly sold out wherever offered.

Waterfowl have much potential as a small-farm enterprise, and their hardy nature makes them attractive to the smallholder with limited, simple facilities. A plastic drum or handful of hay or straw bales piled across each other will create adequate shelter for a small breeding group of ducks or geese.

There are some small acreage–based waterfowl ventures of exceptional size. They primarily operate as hatcheries selling young birds nationally and sometimes even internationally. Such ventures devote extensive time and resources to the marketing process and are heavily dependent on access to U.S. mail for the shipment of their production. That route of shipment was disrupted once, and many still feel it is vulnerable to targeting by animal rights activists and others.

The logical market for the output of a small flock of waterfowl will lie within an hour or two's drive from the farm gate. It is, after all, the farm-to-fork movement that has revived much of the interest in this type of production. It is the area most accessible with direct marketing methods, but so much still depends upon location. My friend near the college town lived in what is termed outstate Missouri but was near enough to fifty thousand–plus people with a substantial disposable income and an exceptional awareness of the food scene. A friend recently moved into north-central Missouri from a smallholding not quite an hour's drive from St. Louis and saw her sales of poultry and small stock chopped by a full two-thirds. She has a long drive back to that area, but still makes it on a fairly regular basis, often to sell to repeat buyers who know her and trust her as their "duck lady." I was recently a part of a seminar with a district representative for one of the nation's most recognizable firms for feed manufacture and sales. She related that the sales for her company's more select lines of poultry feeds fell off dramatically at a point beginning at about fifty miles out from Missouri's two major cities.

I have to believe that that is a statistic that would hold up across much of the country. It is a bit of information that affirms just how crucial the positioning of an alternative poultry venture now is. There are no string men or brokers traveling the countryside to buy surplus fowl for resale, and the loop of major urban markets where live fowl are sold is well traveled by a handful of well-equipped (large trailers) folks bringing birds into them.

The birds are in the country. The buyers are in the cities and the suburbs. In colonial times there were actual drives of large fowl over distances of many miles into the nearest towns of any size. The feet of waterfowl and turkeys were frequently tarred to stand up to the miles to be covered. You don't have to be a duck wrangler now, but to generate good selling prices you do have to know how to wrangle your way to the market.

The breeds of domestic duck familiar to most are the White Pekin and the Rouen. The latter is the large, deep-sided bird with the color pattern similar to that of the wild Mallard. The wild Mallard, or gray, pattern in varying forms is seen on many breeds and reflects the Mallard ancestry of nearly all of the domestic duck breeds.

The main exception to this genetic fact is the Muscovy, the roosting duck from South America. They are a truly interesting breed, and one subject to a great deal of conflict and misinformation. The conflict begins with its very name. Instead of "Mus-co-vee," the correct pronunciation is "Mus-cah-vay." And while a Muscovite hails from Russia, the Muscovy is a native of the southernmost climes.

In this breed the mature males are much larger than the females. They are a duck that doesn't quack, but they do have a serpentine hiss. The face of a good show specimen is heavily encrusted with caruncles, giving it a face only a liquored-up mother could love. The females lay fairly well and are good broodies (several hens may share a nest), and the eggs have a thirty-five-day incubation period. While Muscovies will mate with other breeds, the offspring are often sterile (though fast growing) and are considered to be true mules.

The breed is propagated in a variety of colors including white, black (with white points), blue, and chocolate. A breed feature is the red, fleshy growths—caruncles—on the head and around the beak. These are especially notable on the males as they age. They are growing in value as a meat bird, often harvested primarily for the breast, which many liken to roast beef. The darker feathered birds are the ones that seem to be the most sought after in the ethnic meat bird trade.

Though the White Pekin and the Rouen are perhaps the most familiar of the domestic duck breeds, they are generally seen only in the "industrial" forms rather than those birds that are bred most exactingly to breed standards. The White Pekin was the breed on which the market-leading Long Island duckling was based, and many hatcheries once boasted heavily of the size and dressing qualities of their strain of White Pekin. Well-bred Rouens are also large ducks and are on par with the Aylesbury breed as to being deep sided. It is held that some of the very best of this breed are so deep sided that they can only breed on swimmable water.

Some years ago I interviewed noted midwestern waterfowl breeder Mr. Bill Amundson of Hartford, Michigan. His duck breeds of choice were the Khaki Campbell, Black and White Magpie, and the Chocolate Indian Runner. These three breeds are noted for their vivid coloring, and all three are exceptional egg producers with the Magpie being more of a multi-use bird. With good care, they may lay nearly year-round, and in some earlier flocks Khaki and Runner hens laid up to three hundred eggs per hen per year. The Runner was often likened to the Leghorn, and their unique, upright stance also had them dubbed the "bowling pin" duck by many.

I interviewed another noted waterfowl breeder, Mrs. Frances Grieve of Waco, Texas, at the same time. She noted that the White Pekin breed lays mostly in the spring though early-hatched and some older birds may lay for a short period in the fall as well. The Rouen and Muscovy, she added, follow a similar pattern of lay. I have seen some Muscovy hens produce three clutches of young in a season if the hatchlings are taken away from the hen for artificial brooding.

Among the heavy breeds Mr. Amundson favored the Pekin, the Aylesbury (a very large, white, English breed, with very deep sides and a pink bill and feet), and the Rouen. With a great many of the large breeds there is a seasonal aspect to their egg production, but up and down the United States most should be in or approaching egg production by March first of each year. Mr. Amundson favored the egg-laying breeds for the small farm and holding and gave his Khakis the nod over his Magpies. They produced the eggs that he and his family used and that they sold to others for table use and baking.

The American Poultry Association recognizes seventeen breeds of domestic duck and divides them into four different categories. Included in the heavy breed class are the White Pekin, Aylesbury, Rouen, Muscovy, Saxony, and Silver Appleyard. To catalog and fully describe each breed here would simply take up too much time and space, but we will list a few talking points about some of the newer or less commonly seen varieties.

The Saxony and Silver Appleyard were recognized by the American Poultry Association in 2000 and 1998. The Saxony is a colorful German breed developed in the twentieth century and lays large white-shelled eggs. The male, or drake, has a claret breast, oatmeal-colored body, and a soft blue-gray head. The hen has fawn or buff plumage with white points to the face and neck. They are a quite good-sized duck with mature weights of nine pounds for drakes and eight pounds for hens.

The Silver Appleyard is a breed developed in Great Britain that also lays a large white-shelled egg. They have a color pattern reminiscent of the Mallard. At the end of the mating season the males will molt into "eclipse" plumage that is darker, more mottled, and with grayer tones. They have the same mature weights as the Saxony breed.

A lot of duck breeds were developed to be what are termed "dual-purpose" fowl, which perform as both meat and egg producers. They won't lay as well as the breeds developed as egg layers nor grow and dress as well as birds developed for early harvest as meat birds. A better term, I believe, would be one borrowed from the British: "multi-use fowl." Such birds will do a fair job of both meat and egg production; the species that does not lay and grow does not survive. Still, if your market is for eggs then opt for an egg-laying breed; if your market is for duck meat then breed and produce birds developed to be strong in the traits that contribute to economic duck meat production.

The medium-weight class of duck breeds includes the Cayuga, Crested, Swedish, and Buff. The Crested is bred in Black and White varieties, and a crest is being bred onto other breeds, including the Blue Swedish. There can be real problems with the positioning of the crest, which is to be large, well formed, and centered on the crown of the head. I have seen ducks with crests all over the head and even on the back and sides of the neck. There is also some evidence of health or genetic problems with this trait, and great care must be taken when selecting foundation stock for this breed.

The Swedish breed is now bred in Blue and Black varieties. Blue, or Slate, is always a challenging color to work with in poultry, and this may be one of the reasons for the growing interest in the Black Swedish variety. Either variety must have a white bib that is four to five inches wide at its widest point and tapering in as it moves up toward the mandible. Mature weights are eight pounds for drakes and seven pounds for hen ducks.

There has been a lot of interest in elaborately colored and feathered birds of many different poultry species. They can certainly be eye-catching, and many are bought from artist-recreated pictures in catalogs or on the Internet. Alas, all birds of a breed do not hatch with the potential to be showroom winners; many mismarks can be used to produce later winners, and most will have some practical values. The British will call these garden birds, very suitable for hobbyists or those wanting a few birds to produce for the family table.

It may be a part of reaching just a bit past three score in my number of years, but I see ever greater value in keeping all things simple, including the choice of poultry breeds with which to work. Some colors and patterns are considered extremely difficult challenges even by veteran breeders with decades of experience to draw from. Those seeking to create modest flocks with historical roots and the potential to be bred to be even more productive will find that such birds are often of but a single color and rather simply feathered.

The Buff breed of duck originated on Orpington Farm in England, the seat of breeding for the more well-known Orpington chicken breed. They should have a uniform shade of fawn-buff. In drakes the head and upper neck can vary from fawn-buff to seal brown. Mature weights are the same as for the Swedish breed.

The lightweight group could also be called the egg-laying group and includes the Runner, Khaki Campbell, Magpie, and Welsh Harlequin. The Runner or Indian Runner, the "bottle duck," is noted for its erect stance and egg-laying ability. They were once termed the Leghorns of the duck clan, though they have sense been eclipsed in this regard by the Khaki Campbell.

The Runner has a mature weight of four and a half pounds for drakes and four pounds for hens. Quality can vary widely with these ducks, and when setting out to buy foundation stock shop very carefully for birds with correct structure and durable type. Ducks of this breed are actually used to train and certify herding dogs.

The Runner is bred in a number of colors and patterns including White, Fawn and White, Penciled, Black, Buff, Chocolate, and Gray (Mallard or wild-type coloring). They are a vigorous breed, very animated, and lay a nice-sized egg.

The Khaki Campbell is bred in light and dark brown varietals and a white variety. They have the same mature weights as the Runner and many now deem them the better egg producer of the two. They remind many a bit of the Mallard breed and are popular with smallholders and backyard keepers.

We have kept Khakis of all three varieties and found them to all be productive layers of good-sized eggs with excellent table qualities. We had supper at my in-laws one evening where my father-in-law held fort on how he had no liking for duck eggs and could detect them instantly. My good wife then began tapping a pretty steady tattoo of my shins beneath the table. For the last six months we had been providing them with a mix of eggs from our poultry yard, including a great many Khaki eggs.

The egg-laying breeds are generally non-broody; time on the nest robs from time producing eggs. As a group they tend to have hotter metabolisms and for good egg production need to be fed rations that are well-balanced and with high-quality ingredients.

In the bantam category are the Calls, Black East Indies, and the Mallards. The Calls are the smallest with mature weights of twenty-six ounces for drakes and twenty ounces for hens. They were a breed developed to be living decoys, to quack loudly to "call in" wild ducks, hence the name Call ducks. They have become a true exhibitor's fowl and are bred in a great variety of colors and patterns including Buff, Bibbed Blue, Butterscotch, Chocolate, Gray, Pastel, Snowy, and White. They are most carefully bred for color, diminutive size, and their fine, domed heads. Many that you see are of too large a size or too poor a head type for the breed. They are challenging to breed and are not as productive as most other duck breeds.

The Standard Mallard was derived from the wild Mallard and has a mature weight of forty ounces for drakes and thirty-six ounces for hens. During the summer molt the drakes will lose their vivid coloring and more closely resemble the hens. This is called eclipse feathering and will run through the summer months. There is some confusion about these ducks and you will see references to "tame" Mallards and flying and non-flying Mallards. Wild Mallards are migratory birds protected by a number of state and federal regulations as to their keeping. To be absolutely sure about the regulations for your state consult with state conservation officials. Domestic ducks retain many similarities to their wild forebears and, when mature, are among the hardiest of the poultry species.

Amundson and Grieve, in very different parts of the country, both favored simple three-sided structures or metal huts for housing their breeding birds. They use this plain housing even in the winter months. Over the years I have seen a lot of plastic barrels, reused hog housing, and even some larger doghouses put into use as waterfowl housing. The housing units are set up facing south (most prevailing winds in the United States come from the north or west), and Mr. Amundson would bed his houses with straw, dry leaves, or wood shavings.

Grieve reports good results with a simple housing alternative using six bales of hay or straw stacked two bales high to form a three-sided recess into which the adult birds can shelter or nest. The bales are positioned in an inverted U-shape and are topped with a sheet of exterior plywood weighted to remain in place. After a time in use it can be removed to the compost pile or, with the removal of the plywood sheet, will simply molder away in place. She favors bedding the units with plenty of loose straw or hay so that the birds' feet are well protected from the cold when they huddle down on them and are insulated from the ground. She also recounted a problem with heavy spring rains in her area. In those seasons she uses three sheets of exterior plywood to form an A-frame shelter with the northern or up-slope end blocked by the third sheet. Small, shallow channels can be scooped around such units to direct runoff around and away from the unit. These units shelter nests, feedstuffs, and the birds themselves. An old truck tire can be used in one of these to form the base for a nest.

Whereas housing needs for waterfowl can be kept rather simple, fencing can be quite another matter. Both of these producers related that the greatest problems they had to contend with were losses to predators and roving dogs. A number of different fencing options are available for waterfowl with varying degrees of success. I have seen producers try everything from chain-link fencing to electrically charged strands of smooth wire. Those strands will contain some adult fowl but have to be positioned to assure solid contact with the head and neck area where the shock will have maximal effect.

Grieve raises her waterfowl on about two acres of land with the perimeter fencing being made with five-foot-high horse panels made with four-inch square stay spacings. She also said that chain-link fencing would work well in this role as her primary concern with perimeter fencing was to deter marauding dogs. Divisions for breeding pens can be simpler, but a point of concern in their construction is the use of materials with such a fine mesh or spacings as to cause the birds' heads to become trapped or caught and twisted, thus injuring or even killing the birds.

Mrs. Grieve favored forty-eight-inch-high chicken wire with one-inch octagonal spacings for forming interior pens. This kind of wire will need substantial bracing and framing and will have to be inspected often for breakdown or damage. This type of wire is now available with several forms of coating and in heights up to six feet. It is still rather easily entered by larger predators. Though more costly, one-by-two-inch or even two-by-four-inch square mesh is made with heavier gauge wire and will prove more durable. I have even seen wooden palleting given a second life forming enclosures for some of the heavier varieties of waterfowl not prone to flight.

A growing number of waterfowl breeders are using plastic doghouses and kennel panels to contain small numbers of waterfowl. A ten-foot-by-ten-foot four-panel pen with walk-through gate can be bought new for three hundred dollars or less. Searching the local want ads and online can often reveal some real buys of used kennel equipment. I was once given two such units simply for taking them down and removing them from the owner's property. These units are easily moved about and will contain a couple of trios of ducks or a trio of geese. They are one of the most predator-proof containment systems (they were designed to hold in canines) and require very little maintenance. They work very well where space is at a premium and may make it possible to fit in small numbers of waterfowl where ordinances are most stringent.

Predator control has always been the bane of poultry producers, running the gamut from hawks and owls that attack from the sky to rats and weasels that can crawl through knotholes to dogs and coyotes that can go over or under many types of fencing. The ideal type of fencing has often been described as horse high, bullhorn strong, and baby chick tight. Unfortunately the cost of such fencing would indicate that it's made of gold, too. A steel box would be true predator-proof protection, but it would not be conducive to growth or reproduction.

There are a number of predator control options that can be employed, often in unison, to better protect the flocks on the family farm or small-holding. Geese and guineas can actually be employed as an early warning system of the arrival of predators and other intruders on the scene. Pen tops can also be employed to protect breeding groups and youngsters from flying and climbing predators.

Many are reporting good results with Great Pyrenees and other guardian dog breeds raised with and imprinted on poultry. We have a friend that raises such dogs and with two patrolling her small farm has had virtually no predator loss of ranging birds. They will even bark at flying predators and rush at them should they attempt to set down in their territory. They have to be free to patrol the whole premises, however, as predators quickly learn the limited reach of a chained or kenneled dog.

A growing number of producers are using those red light boxes to counter nighttime predator losses, but they must be used carefully. The fixed red lights are believed to resemble the eyes of a larger creature, but they need to be moved often lest the vermin catch on. Bears and panthers don't stand night after night staring from the same points around the property.

Many will pen their birds in the more heavily traveled parts of the barnyard and in lighted areas, such as under dusk-to-dawn lights. It can help, but we once lost birds to a coon that would take down birds in pens right outside our bedroom window. A couple of Feist-type dogs now loll and patrol there each evening.

The attentive producer can do much to check predator losses just as he is going about his daily chores. Pens can be given timely repair, early signs of vermin intrusion noted and bait stations set out, litter and clutter that can harbor vermin should be removed, the birds should be monitored several times each day, and a regular human presence on the scene will do much to deter predators.

Spraying ammonia around pens and coops is said to repel raccoons, but other deterrents, such as playing a radio, are often quickly figured out by these wily creatures. Charged electrical wires at heights of four and twelve inches above the ground will help to deter some predators. The best offense against predators will probably be a mix of many things.

The belief that all waterfowl absolutely have to have swimmable water for good reproduction to occur is widespread but mistaken. This is true for a handful of very deep-sided, heavy weight breeds and swans, but not for most of the more commonly kept waterfowl. I have seen non-flying Mallards breed, lay, brood, and rear clutches of young entirely in wire mesh–floored pens.

Water is nevertheless a natural part of these birds' element and should be provided to them in good amounts and a clean manner. It will add to their comfort and sense of well-being, and protection from some predators can be afforded by swimming well out into larger ponds and lakes. This protection is lost, however, when those bodies of water begin to ice over. And it is a pleasure to watch them on water. White Chinese geese are lovely on the water, and some call them the poor man's swan.

It is essential to offer water in containers to a depth that the birds can at least immerse their heads for grooming and to keep the bill and nostrils free of any detritus picked up while feeding. Water can be provided in rubber tubs or other devices with a depth of six to eight inches. Such pans will hold three to five gallons of water, are easily cleaned, and the water can be changed often to keep it clean. Adult waterfowl will consume rather substantial amounts of drinking water.

Producers have employed a great many different systems to provide water to ducks and geese. I have seen waterfowl penned alongside small streams and even small streams diverted to run through waterfowl pens. I suspect that state conservation agencies would have something to say about those practices now. Many ponds were once sectioned into pie slice segments with woven wire that then fanned out onto the bank to create numerous pens for waterfowl around such a body of water. Some will provide in each pen a hand poured cement basin that will hold five to ten gallons of water. These can easily be flip cleaned with an old shovel or broom.

Inexpensive plastic kiddie wading pools have been used by many to provide water in waterfowl pens of some size. They are partially filled, are easy to clean, and will last for three years or more with reasonable care. It is hard to beat those black rubber pans with a capacity of about three gallons for providing water to just about any kind of poultry. They are durable, can be bleached often as a sanitary measure, are modestly priced, and can be used year round. Should the contents freeze it is a simple matter to flip the pans over and free the ice load with a few sharp blows to the sides and bottom.

The key to waterfowl management is not how the water is provided but keeping it clean and fresh. To that end the containers must be simple to drain and easy to rinse clean. In hot weather water may need to be changed as often as two or three times each day. The stale water should be removed in a way that will not create mud or unsanitary conditions in or near the pen. Yes, the waterfowl may dabble and splash their water about, but there are measures that the producer can that will help to maintain the sanitary aspects.

If the ducks have to reach up and in to water they will sling it around less. Waterers and pans can be placed on pallets or platforms that quickly drain. And it may be necessary to move the water points around often to prevent mud problems from forming.

Both of the breeders cited here recommend that beginners with ducks keep their initial efforts small and invest only in high-quality birds from which to begin a breeding program. They also shared the opinion that it is best to begin with just one breed and no more than two. This thinking fits handily with the industry norm of selling and shipping ducklings in lots of ten to fifteen as-hatched ducklings. From a good source/breeder such a group should produce one good trio of breeding quality (show quality is a whole other thing and not what we are addressing here) and a backup pair or two. Holding back that second male for insurance can sometimes save a whole year and a lot of frantic effort if the only male retained is lost.

For best results the breeding groups should be kept small and in separate pens. The breeding in such contained groups can be kept clear, is easily tracked, and is in keeping with the use of smaller containment systems such as dog kennels. Mr. Amundson reports good fertility with as many as four to five hens penned with one drake in the lighter weight breeds. Trios and three-and-ones may be the best way to go to better assure fertility levels and especially so with the heavier breeds.

With lighter weight goose breeds one gander may be kept with as many as three or four hens. With some of the heavier breeds, however, such as well-bred Toulouse, they will breed satisfactorily only in pairs. And such birds may not produce any eggs in fertile numbers until they are three years old. Where freely ranged, geese of the lighter breeds may be set out in groups of six to twelve hens and three or four ganders. Breeding waterfowl should be regularly monitored for vigor, soundness, and obesity—all can impact reproductive performance. Old, heavier males will not perform as well, though there are records of some geese producing fertile eggs into their second decade. Younger males will be more agile and less damaging to females. An excess number of males in the group can also cause problems.

Pedigreed matings will require small breeding pens headed up by a single male and often rely on pair matings. When broken into small groups the poor performers are more quickly and easily spotted. Being able to track eggs and the resultant young back to the breeding unit that produced them will facilitate culling and hasten the removal of poor-performing individuals and lines from the flock. One poor-performing female in a pen camouflaged by a number of good performers will cost the producer every day that she lives and can even set a breeding program back by precious years.

The needs of local markets may be adequately met with the production of but one or two well-performing trios of breeding birds. While color and other novelty factors can influence demand for a short time, the real factors in building flocks and the markets they serve are quality, producer expertise, and his or her dependable presence.

Goslings are generally sold in as-hatched lots of six to eight with sexing, where available, adding five to six dollars to the price of each bird.

Good goslings are expensive, and I know many who have spent $150.00 and more for a trio of very well-bred goslings. That is a big bite into the wallet, and you will very seldom equal those prices when selling into more localized markets. It will, however, often take foundation stock of that quality to gain entrance into and hold a position in local markets.

Geese and ducks will begin laying fairly early in the year as the days lengthen and begin to warm. Two-by-two-foot nest boxes with four-to-six inch-high sides set at ground level or large truck tires filled with a good nesting material such as wheat straw will make practical nesting units. Sadly, a few waterfowl females seem to emerge each year that will lay wherever and whenever the whim hits them, including right at the waterline of the nearest pond. This may be caused in part by overcrowding, stress, or general poor care with no other options provided to the hens. It will be seen most often with the first few eggs laid. These eggs, when found, are generally too chilled and soiled to be retained for hatching.

Waterfowl aren't the best of housekeepers under any circumstances, and the producer might often be confronted with chilled and soiled eggs. A strawed lot, containment in the house until mid to late morning, and frequent egg collection will all be necessary. Some soiling can be lightly scraped or rubbed from the egg shells, but excessively soiled or stained eggs should not be placed in the incubator. There the bacteria on them might grow and kill the germ in surrounding eggs, and require extensive cleaning and disinfection of the unit.

Some will not place waterfowl eggs in incubators used for other species. They can be especially challenging to hatch in the smaller table-top incubators. The art of hatching waterfowl eggs can spark conversations among veteran producers that will go on for hours. Some tips on waterfowl egg management for incubation include:

1. Gather the eggs often, three or more times each day, especially in cold weather.
2. Discard any badly stained or fouled eggs. If you wouldn't eat it, don't try to incubate it.
3. Discard eggs that have been chilled for any length of time or that cannot be verified for freshness.
4. Store for no more than five to ten days before incubation. Store in a cool area at temperatures of forty-five to sixty degrees Fahrenheit. Turn the eggs often to prevent the air spaces from sticking in the shell. The removable plastic racks that are used to hold waterfowl eggs in cabinet incubators work well for holding eggs that will not fit chicken egg cartons or flats.

5. Light staining can be removed from the shell with gentle scraping by a blunt-edged blade or light sanding with a fine grit sand paper.

6. This is, I know, a controversial point, but when we were supplying eggs to a nearby hatchery we were required to wash them in water to which a small amount of household bleach had been added. We added a teaspoon of bleach to a quart of water 103°F or a bit warmer. The eggs were placed in the water for thirty seconds or less and wiped dry and clean with a soft cloth. Yes, it is a controversial practice, but water of this temperature should not cause anything to be drawn through the pores in the egg shell. We changed the water and solution often, and the hatchery owner regularly reported hatches of 90+ percent with eggs handled this way.

7. Before going into the incubator the eggs should be candled to detect any fine shell cracks or other problems.

8. Incubators should be thoroughly cleaned and disinfected after each setting of waterfowl eggs. Carefully remove any unhatched waterfowl eggs from the incubator cabinet lest they break and further soil the interior of the cabinet.

Mr. Amundson did not have an incubator and took his eggs to be custom hatched (a sideline venture to be considered in areas where fairly substantial numbers of poultry are being produced from small flocks). Mrs. Grieve preferred using moving air incubators and had two cabinet models of her own.

A producer in our area has mastered the task of hatching fair numbers of waterfowl eggs in small, still-air Styrofoam incubators. These units have gotten better in design and operation in recent years but still require a good bit of attention when in use. I strongly suspect that he replaces the bottom halves of these units quite often as they become too soiled to easily clean. Some now have replaceable plastic liners that cost just about as much as new bottoms ($10.00–$15.00).

Sears used to sell an all-metal table-top incubator with a higher top element to accommodate goose and larger duck eggs. Replacement parts for such units can still be bought from numerous supply houses, and a farmstead auction in our area cannot be considered complete unless one of the little metal units is in the sale order. These high-domed units were called "goosers," and I'll leave you to make your own joke.

Operating an incubator is a lot like owning an old tractor or pickup.

You have to learn its rhythms and idiosyncrasies and work with and within them for best results. Waterfowl eggs, due to their larger size and longer incubation times, are always going to be more of a challenge to hatch. With smaller incubators, hatching rates of 45 percent or so are considered quite good, and they demand that a close eye be kept both on the eggs going into it and the unit when in operation. Even more than with chickens, many will opt to maintain separate units for incubating and hatching waterfowl eggs, and both will require a though cleaning after each use.

Although most duck eggs take twenty-eight days to hatch, Muscovy eggs will require thirty-five days. Eggs may hatch a day or even two earlier or later depending on air temperature. Eggs held in very hot weather may even go into a state of early or pre-incubation that will affect their hatching time. Muscovy ducks are among the most challenging to hatch in an incubator, possibly due in part to their large size or longer incubation period. If allowed to do so, several Muscovy hens may lay to a single nest. Some breeders will leave Muscovy duck eggs under a hen for two to three weeks before placing them in an incubator and report better results by doing so.

Humidity and temperature management can be a real juggling act with waterfowl eggs. Many producers have their own tricks and techniques for hatching waterfowl eggs, and they can spark a lot of debate. One garnering much discussion right now is whether to incubate the eggs lying on their sides and cushioned in the trays with bits of cloth or to incubate them small-end down in the incubator trays.

Another practice that draws much discussion is the cooling of duck and goose eggs in the latter stages of the incubation process. In natural incubation the female will leave the nest for a period of time each day. This is so she can eat, drink, and defecate. It is for a period commonly held to be of about thirty minutes in duration. Beginning somewhere between the fifteenth and twentieth day of incubation some producers will withdraw eggs from the incubator for fifteen to thirty minutes each day. They are left to stand at room temperature before being returned to the incubator. In a forced-air incubator, if possible, the fan should be turned off before entering the cabinet to prevent a heightened loss of heat and humidity. This is an added step that will take time and is probably best resolved by each producer based on his or her unit, location, and climate.

Mrs. Grieve turned her waterfowl eggs twice each day in her small incubators. Incubators with automatic turners will generally turn the eggs three or more times each day. To facilitate turning by hand, place large Xs and Os on opposite sides of each egg with light pencil strokes. A light pass of the hand over the eggs should give the desired half turn quickly, and the emergence of a new side's symbol each time will assure that they are all being turned.

Mrs. Grieve prefers to have the eggs lying on their sides in the incubator and daily tops out the water pans in the incubators to maintain proper humidity. To add water to the channels beneath the eggs in the Styrofoam units, some producers will place a small funnel in one of the air holes in the tops of the units, attach a short length of tubing to the small end in the incubator, and position it to direct water into the channel beneath the eggs. It should be positioned to not interfere with the automatic turner. Providing water without opening the unit will allow better temperature and humidity management.

The water used in the cabinet should be at room temperature or a bit warmer. Most water drawn straight from a deep well will average fifty-five degrees Fahrenheit and will pull down temperatures inside the incubator. As her duck eggs go into the incubator, Mrs. Grieve will write on each with light pencil strokes the breed, pen number that produced them, and the date they went into the incubator. Under her system you turn the date side up in the morning and down in the evening.

After the first week in the incubator, the eggs can be candled regularly to assure that the embryos are developing correctly. Any eggs that are not developing should be removed from the incubator and discarded. Small incubators need to be placed in an area where temperatures remain fairly constant around sixty degrees Fahrenheit as fluctuations outside of the incubator of even a few degrees can have impact on hatching rates.

Baby ducks and geese are fragile creatures, and they need to be tended and managed accordingly. They can have real problems with dampness and chill, and an unsanitary environment can lead quickly to problems with *E. coli* and other ills. In the brooder unit they need to be kept warm and dry, protected from drafts, and have non-slip surfaces upon which to walk.

For his brooding units, Mr. Amundson used old livestock water tanks that might no longer be watertight. He would level them; cover the bottoms with one and a half inches of shavings, peat moss, or ground corn cobs; suspend a 250-watt heat bulb at least eighteen inches above the hatchlings at one end of the old tank; and then cover the tank tops with one-inch poultry mesh. This is a widely used method of poultry brooding, and some will cover the tanks with old window screens weighted to stay in place. He kept his ducklings in such units for two to three weeks. Some thoughts on getting ducklings off to a good start include:

1. Keep the litter clean and dry. Any wet areas should be promptly removed and fresh litter added each day. Keeping the brooder area dry can be a challenge, but it will create a much better environment for that all-important early growth.

2. Use the birds as indicators when hanging the heat lamp. If they are huddled together directly beneath it they are cold and the lamp is suspended too high. If they are crowded into the corners at a distance from the lamp it is suspended too low and they are too warm. At the right height the birds will contentedly go about their business eating, drinking, and resting.

3. Start the newly arrived or hatched birds on drinking water gradually over a period of a couple of hours. Do not allow them to drink their fill too quickly. Young waterfowl should not be allowed to run out of drinking water, either. If you find empty waterers, bring them back slowly over a period of time. Young waterfowl can drink excessively in such situations and then succumb to a sort of water intoxication.

4. Never suspend the heat lamps by their cords. Use either steel wire or lightweight chain to suspend them. There should never be more than seven 259-watt heat bulbs operating on a single circuit.

5. To reduce waste and cut down on dampness elevate feeders and waterers on simple ten-inch-by-ten-inch or twelve-inch-by-twelve-inch risers made with two-inch-by-two-inch stock and hardware cloth. Make simple, open frames with the stock, and top them with the hardware cloth. Center the feeders and waterers atop these low risers. Waste and water loss is reduced because the birds have to raise their heads up and in to eat and drink. Much of the water that gets splashed out falls through the hardware cloth and is better contained there, away from the young birds.

6. Use tepid drinking water for the first couple of days and teach the newly arrived birds how to drink by dipping their beaks into the fountain bases a couple of times. The waterers should be rinsed and refilled twice each day. For the safety of the young birds the waterer lips should be quite shallow.

7. Young waterfowl should not be brooded with other young poultry.

8. Starter feeds were once hard to find for young waterfowl. Many chick starters had additives that ducklings simply could not handle, and any feeds with antibiotics and most other additives should not be used with young waterfowl. They can handle the coccidiosis preventative Amprolin that is included in many chick starters. Game bird starters often have too much protein content, and problems with wing development, such as angel wing, can occur. Now a great many feed companies do offer a starter/grower formulated for heavier birds that will work when starting waterfowl, turkeys, and heavy breed chickens.

A few brief points on assembling and managing breeding ducks might be in order here:

1. Artificial lighting can be used to increase early season duck egg production. This could be especially needed for flocks supplying a hatchery or meeting an early season market such as the Easter trade.
2. The ratio of drakes to hens in a group of as-hatched ducklings is roughly one to one. The smaller the group ordered, the more likely it can skew heavily toward one sex or the other. Many old hands believe twenty ducklings to be a good number with which to begin when launching a breeding flock.
3. Depending on breed, a hen duck may begin laying by as early as five months of age. Most breeds have received little in the way of selective breeding for egg-laying performance in recent years. One thing that can be said for show breeders is that females generally do not enter their breeding pens until they have had time to fully develop and prove themselves in the showroom. Old chicken hands would not save setting hens from a female until her second year of production. She was given the time to prove herself a productive performer as free of faults as possible. By being on the farm longer she also had the time to build up her natural immunity to the particular "bug" mix on that farm and was better able to pass it on to her young. Many hatcheries now start the year with young pullet stock. This is done to pare production costs as older stock is sold at the end of the market year, and there is then no added wintering cost.
4. In a breeding pen a duck should have ten to twenty-five square feet of space and summer shade either from existing trees or simple lean-to structures.

5. A duck nest should be twelve inches by sixteen to eighteen inches, and there should be at least one nest for every four to five hens.
6. A duck hen in lay will consume .5 to .6 pounds of feed daily. They should also be offered a good source of grit free-choice.

A creature with what appears to be a shovel for a mouth ought to be able to eat anything, but they should be fed for good health and optimum performance even when kept in the smallest of numbers on the smallest of holdings.

Feed quality is critical whether you are feeding for growth and meat production or egg output. My 1951 copy of Frank Morrison's *Feeds and Feeding* lists this formula for one ton of an 18 percent crude protein content breeding duck ration: 425 pounds of ground yellow corn, 300 pounds of wheat bran, 200 hundred pounds of wheat standard middlings, 300 pounds of wheat red dog, 200 pounds of low fiber ground oats, 150 pounds of soybean meal, 75 pounds of meat scraps, 120 pounds of alfalfa meal, 150 pounds of dried skim milk, 70 pounds of pulverized limestone, and 10 pounds of salt.

Go to your local feed store with that formula and see what happens. After explaining to them what wheat red dog is, you will discover that many of the rest of the ingredients are no longer available. This corner doesn't think that feeding soybean oil meal is a sin and is probably an economic necessity for a great many small-scale producers. And I still buy into the old-timers' argument that it takes feeding some meat to make meat, but this is not the place for those arguments. This does show that a lot of what is called progress really isn't and that one of the things that factory farming is all about is reducing producer options. Consumer wants will certainly affect how meat and eggs are produced now, but many will come at substantial costs both to the producer and the consumer. The organic cherry on the cupcake don't come cheap!

Some larger feed companies do make a waterfowl starter as a special-order product that must be ordered in lots of often one to three tons. Frances Grieve endorsed a Purina product, Meat Builder, as a good waterfowl starter. That product has been reformulated for even broader use with several larger-sized poultry species and is now marketed as Flock Raiser.

When her young ducks were about a month old, Grieve started mixing in some scratch grains and non-medicated hog grower complete ration (this is typically a pelleted feed product with a crude protein content in the 14–17 percent range). In times of very high feed prices, poultry producers with many different species have turned to a similar swine feed product to pare costs. Some swine feeds are comparable to poultry feeds but will need supplementation with calcium and grit at least. And such changes should be made gradually and only after much study. Chopped lettuce or spinach in quarter-inch-sized pieces can also be fed to young birds. Offer no more of this than can be cleaned up in a period of ten to fifteen minutes a couple of times a day.

Grieve pointed out that niacin is one of the greatest needs in waterfowl breeding rations. To formulate a breeder ration to use with her birds she combined three parts Purina Layena (a widely available, complete layer ration for chickens) to one part each of rolled, steamed oats; shelled corn; wheat; and non-medicated rabbit pellets. As an added measure, she would sometimes soak the oats overnight in wheat germ or fish oils before mixing them with the other components a couple of times each week.

Most of the poultry producers I have met over the years tweak their birds' rations in one way or another. Some contend they have developed über-performing secret ingredients, but most are simply adding a bit of greenery or boosting protein levels when performance needs to be bolstered or increased. To me a part of the fun and challenge of poultry keeping has been to find the little things that will help our birds perform better on our small farm.

A ranging bird will consume many things that do not make it into the nutrition texts, occasionally with disastrous results. Still, I believe that we may not yet know all that we might about livestock nutrition; those old-timers feeding their poultry homegrown or locally produced feedstuffs were onto something. Skimmed milk; high-protein, open-pollinated corn; meat scrap; and good hay formed the backbone of feeding systems back when poultry production was big business on a great number of the nation's farms.

Mrs. Grieve also made available to her birds good-quality alfalfa hay offered in above-the-head feeders made from two-inch-spaced poultry mesh. The ducks had to reach up pull out leafy bits of the good quality hay to eat. Offering hay to poultry in this manner leaves much less waste than typical feeding practices. When her breeding birds were not in production she fed them a maintenance ration of 14 percent crude protein hog grower pellets in the morning and offered a simple mix of oats and wheat later in the day.

Mr. Amundson noted that by maintaining a plan of good facility sanitation and avoiding moldy and medicated feedstuffs, his flock's health problems had been "just about nonexistent." Mrs. Grieve dealt with the problem of open wounds with an aerosol astringent such as Blue Lotion. Allowing a bird with foot injury or a limp access to a child's pool seemed to hasten healing.

The other side of the waterfowl coin is the production of geese, the giants of the poultry yard. They are among the very best of avian foragers, gleaning spilt grain behind cattle and eating grass and weeds in places far too difficult to reach by mechanical means. Their bill design and digestive system are such that they can better utilize graze than any other poultry species. They are not quite "open the gate and let 'em go" stock, but once fully feathered they get close to being bomb proof and tend to be vulnerable only to the largest of predators and marauding dogs

My grandmother had a Gray hen goose that she would actually dress in a little bonnet and apron that followed her around like a dog. This goose apparently hated me. The old rip had a game that could be called "run Kelly through the back screen door." She pursued it only periodically, by whim apparently, and she was good at it. I became quite fit as a youngster as a result, but also a bit twitchy.

Geese essentially fall into two groups: those that are descended from the wild Swan goose of Asia and those bred from the Graylag in Europe. Geese produce modest numbers of young each year when compared to most other poultry services. A hen goose may lay just sixty to one hundred eggs each year, and some larger varieties and tightly bred show birds may lay even less. They are very seasonal in their laying, which goes hand in glove with meat geese being most often targeted to the holiday markets late in the year. A lot of English majors each year set out to have a goose for Christmas dinner in honor of Mr. Charles Dickens.

The most commonly seen descendants of the Swan goose are the African and the Chinese. The African has no roots in that continent, but it does take its name from the long-ago, near-folk practice of attributing anything new or exotic on the livestock front to that continent. The African is one of the largest of the domestic goose varieties and the Chinese one of the smallest. Both have a distinctive knob above the bill. Waterfowl have bills and not beaks. The African is most common in its Brown-feathered form, although it is now being bred in Buff and White varietals. The Chinese is more widely seen in White feathering, although there is also a Brown varietal.

The Chinese just may be the best layer of all of the goose breeds, with some hens laying over one hundred eggs per year. They are also among the most active of the goose breeds and are certainly one of the most vocal. As Dad used to say, "They like to holler."

Goose eggs are edible, although two over easy will leave little room on the plate for ham and hashbrowns. They have most of the same cooking qualities as a duck egg, although some claim that they have a bit more of a "texture" issue. I know of no goose egg trade per se, and most raisers view the egg in the same way the goose does: the goose egg is the way to get another goose.

The goose varieties bred from the Graylag include the Toulouse, Gray, Buff, Pilgrim, Shetland, and Sebastopol. Some are also bred with a tuft of head feathers.

There are a number of other varieties bred in Europe, and there are some rare breeds here, such as the Pomeranian, which is bred in both gray and buff varieties. Some "breeds" have much-discussed genetic backgrounds, like the Cotton Patch and the Blue. In Europe some short-billed varieties were even bred for fighting. Geese can live for many years and maintain at least some level of productivity for a great many of them, and small pockets of rare and old-line genetics do pop up from time to time.

Much controversy now surrounds what exactly is and isn't a Toulouse goose. The breed is of French origin, and the better-bred specimens do grow to truly mammoth proportions. A top male may crowd sixty pounds. They have a true dewlap, do not reach breeding maturity till the age of three, lay a very modest number of eggs, and are very much not a breed for beginners.

What is still being termed a Toulouse in many corners is coming to more and more be called a Gray goose. They will reach sexual maturity by one year of age, there is no dewlap, and the coloring is dark gray along the upper body moving to lighter gray down on the bird with some white tip coloring appearing in the rear area. The Gray goose, with its orange bill and feet, is the breed with which most of us are familiar. They have a mature weight of twenty-plus pounds for the ganders and twenty pounds or less for the better-bred hens. This is the goose most seen patrolling the farmyard and swimming in local ponds, the hissing and honking birds that chased us when we were kids.

Perhaps this is the place to make a point or two about goose behavior. I have been chased, popped with wing butts, and nipped, and I try to give these big birds the respect they are due. They aren't feathered pit bulls. Most domestic geese can't fly; they have short legs that are powerful for swimming but not much for speed on land. Their hissing and displays are thus defensive mechanisms. I once helped to catch some three-quarter-grown geese that were half Canada, and they postured like tigers but were calm and easy to handle once in hand. The hissing, the neck extending, and the charging behavior are all the efforts of a fairly small creature to look bigger and nastier than most predators would want to take on in a fight. Their honking and energetic responses to intruders have earned them a place as feathered wardens of the farmyard and village dating all the way back to Roman times.

Some lines and even some breeds are less aggressive than others, but being a goose is something you can't hold against a goose. Some of the most docile goose with which I ever worked were Pilgrims that actually ate from my hand from a young age. Not long ago I witnessed a pair of young Shetland geese remaining almost stoic in a smaller pen at a big farm show with thousands of passersby.

Many times geese will pair bond and both will defend the nest, unlike duck pairs in which the hen is generally left entirely on her own. A Chinese male may mate with two or possibly even three hens, but most heavy geese are kept in pairs. Separate penning of the breeders will be needed for pedigreed matings; this will facilitate egg collection and quality, and fertility may be improved.

Goose is the classic table bird for holiday meals in England and many parts of Europe. Here, however, most consumers have little or no experience with domestic goose on the plate and rare and often bad experiences with poorly handled wild goose. In the United States the goose may be the definitive niche role player in poultry production. And a very small niche it is.

Building a goose-based venture and any kind of goose market is going to ask a lot of the producer, involve a great deal in the way of information sharing, and involve almost all small-lot sales. Last fall I saw a pair of young African geese sell for one hundred dollars, and one or two more pairs could have possibly been sold over the course of that three-day event. There can be some small-lot sales of goslings or hatching eggs early in the year. Geese are a bit of a hard sell at our local bird markets, especially surplus males, and there are some largely one-time sales of a handful of geese as pond ornaments.

When we kept geese there was a breeding/laying season fairly early in the year, a set or two of goslings to get started, young geese to grow out, and then the retained adults to be taken through the long fall and winter months. For many months of the year geese can maintain themselves on good-quality, fine-stemmed grass and a bit of supplemental grain. That option evaporates in the cold months, and geese will need fair amounts of grain and protein supplement to maintain themselves. Young and growing geese will need lots of supplementation even in good grass-growing weather, and breeding geese in lay will need added feed.

Geese will generally perform well on the same rations described for ducks, although the amounts consumed daily will be greater in correlation with their greater size. Some feed companies do offer complete rations that can be fed to geese and other large fowl varieties. Consult with your local feed suppliers as to what is available in the various lines of feed they can source. Consolidation and mergers now have feed companies having access to feed lines and products not normally seen and used in the local area.

Too much protein in a growing ration can cause a problem with misshapen wing feathers in the fast-developing youngsters, called angel wing. It can sometimes be corrected by taping the feathers back in place if caught soon enough.

If you have found a market for some ducks, you may have found an opening sell some geese. From the standpoint of meat production the market will be very seasonable from late fall into early winter. Birds hatched in late spring will fill this need, and most hatcheries will halt offering goslings by mid-June.

The best way to start a goose venture would be with eight to twelve goslings of the best quality you can find that your budget can be stretched to cover. Currently that will represent an investment of between $150 and perhaps $400, including shipping. That may sound like a good bit for something swathed in down that will fit on the pickup seat next to you; however, it can be the start to a lifetime venture and should gain you access to some of the best genetics of in the field. And as one old hand in the poultry game told me, "Bub, you sure ain't gonna buy much of a heifer for just three or four bills."

From time to time you will see adult geese at an auction or bird swap, but one has to weigh the purchase of such birds quite carefully. The thinking is that unless it is a dispersal of the flock, the best birds are left at home, and if it is a dispersal, why? Early in the year such birds may cost fifty dollars or more each, and this is only fair as the seller has borne the effort of wintering the large birds and their equally large appetites.

And there are challenges even to evaluating a large bird. They are not the easiest of birds to sex on sight, even when well grown. Vent sexing is probably the easiest done on geese of all poultry species, but a goose is not the easiest of birds to handle. Some look for a few visual tells on the sexing of geese. For example, a longer, thicker neck and a head held higher and straighter is said to be indicative of a male. Two breeds of goose, the Pilgrim and the Shetland, are auto-sexing. That is, the males hatch and feather in one color and the females another. The males are white (yellowish down at hatching) and will feather white with a few gray patches on the neck. The females will hatch with a gray down and grow into a typical Gray goose appearance. They are among the smaller goose breeds, with the Pilgrim having an adult weight of fourteen pounds for the gander and thirteen pounds for the goose. The Shetlands are not yet recognized by the American Poultry Association and are smaller still than the Pilgrims.

Past the gosling stage, a goose may be the most capable of all poultry species to fend for itself. The housing options outlined for ducks will work with geese, and some goose hens will be inclined to build their nests close to water. Alas, that also puts them much closer to most predators.

When laying, geese should be contained to better maintain egg condition and freshness if going into an incubator. A single pair can be contained in a modest pen made with a few cattle panels (fifty-four inches high by sixteen feet long). A fifty-five-gallon drum with one end cut out, laid on its side, staked into place, and bedded with straw will make a good shelter and nesting site. A large doghouse will also work well. A goose, if allowed to brood her own eggs, will face the opening to her nest to defend against intruders. Both drums and doghouses are conducive to this aspect of natural goose behavior.

With that initial purchase of eight to twelve goslings one can gain a lot of much-needed hands-on experience, have a few birds with which to test the interest level of a local market, and produce a couple of pairs of breeders from which to launch a farm flock. Some hatcheries will sex their goslings for a cost of around two dollars each, although they may require the purchase of at least one male with every two to three females. It might be wise to purchase eight goslings from two clearly different sources. It will give you two lines to work with, and those genetics can then be combined to create the needed line for that farm or smallholding.

∽

Not long ago I fielded a phone call from a lady planning to retire to Hawaii where even the most basic of feedstuffs can be quite expensive. We went through a number of options for her to consider from the poultry kingdom, including chicken breeds, such as the Cubalaya, that were developed for life on islands in the Caribbean. Then I remembered that the state bird of Hawaii is the rare Nene goose, that denizen of the islands and crossword puzzles. Geese presented perhaps the best option for her as they can graze to meet much of their nutritional needs in a warm climate. It was also handy that some of the nation's largest and highest-regarded waterfowl hatcheries are situated on the West Coast of the United States.

Being natural weeders, geese have been used to keep things trim around barnyards and to help check weeds growing in crops as diverse as cotton, strawberries, herbs, and pine seedlings. They also work well in orchards and like ducks have demonstrated some effectiveness in controlling snail populations. They were once commonly dry plucked as live birds for their down. Three birds will produce about a pound of down, a valuable insulating material in both bedding and garments.

Waterfowl breeders Mr. Bill Amundsen of Hartford, Michigan, and Mrs. Francis Grieve of Waco, Texas, are true, purebred producers of select waterfowl. Their efforts and goals are essentially the same as those who work with pedigreed Black Angus cattle or Suffolk sheep. Their primary concern is bird quality and their income potential hinges upon maintaining that quality, desirability, and recognition into the marketplace.

Amundsen favors the Pilgrim, Buff, and Brown Chinese breeds, with the Pilgrim breed getting his nod as the choice for beginners and small-scale producers. This is an auto-sexing breed with a high profile among poultry raisers now. Personal experience with them attests that they are among the gentlest of the goose tribe. We grew out several on small sun-porches, and they would feed from our hands with no nibbled fingers.

The ganders are always white with some small, gray spotting on the neck and saddle sometimes appearing, and the females are always gray with a bit of white in the face possible. Mrs. Grieve favors the Brown Chinese and Pilgrim breeds as well, but her third breed choice is the Brown African. It is one of the largest of the goose breeds with a very distinctive dark knob above the bill.

Both of the producers report sales of hatching eggs, goslings, and breeding pairs from their well-known and highly regarded flocks of purebred geese. They report local feed stores as being good outlets for some of their surplus goslings, and extra eggs can be used for the table.

For those selling purebred poultry to other farmers and smallholders, one of the modern enigmas has been just how hard it is to sell white- or solid black-feathered birds. Most predators are opportune feeders, and there is no study of which I am aware that shows raccoons and chicken hawks have expressed breed or color preferences. Especially with the alternative poultry varieties, eye appeal is very much a selling factor, and the birds have to look the part to bring the price. I have always been partial to white-feathered birds, and you will generally always find some around our poultry yard. Still, the small-scale producer has to be every bit as mindful of what drives the market as the high-volume producer if he or she is to succeed.

I have a friend with a flock of bred-in-the-purple Emden geese, a flock that has been in existence for decades and is deep in Sherraw breeding. It is his flock of Africans, however, that draws the most attention when new and inexperienced folks visit his farm. With alternative poultry ventures the heart wants what the heart wants, and if you give a Chevy pickup to a Ford man he will never be really happy with it.

The marketing season for breeding and replacement waterfowl falls mainly in the spring. Mrs. Grieve reports that by mid-May markets for both ducklings and goslings fall off sharply in her area. Established breeders are often able to sustain and supply localized markets with just a couple of distinctive breeds kept in two or three small breeding groups (pairs or trios) of each. Alternative poultry production is a lot like telling jokes; it is always better to leave your audience wanting more.

The back-to-the-land movement and interest in local, sustainable agriculture seems to have done much to revive the fortunes of local, smaller-sized commercial hatcheries. Such businesses are not always able to produce for themselves all of the different poultry varieties they might like to offer their customers. They may thus be an approachable market for hatching eggs from some of the alternative poultry varieties produced on your farm. Most are open to inquiries from reputable producers of good, purebred stock. You must, however, be prepared to back up your claims, open your flocks to inspection, and be willing to produce in the time frame and for the demands of their markets. Most of these businesses will pay for the eggs upon pickup and will assist with management questions and the acquisition of further seedstock. They won't pay Internet auction prices for hatching eggs but will buy in volume, cooperate with delivery, and can be considered a dependable outlet for the course of the hatching season. Their needs are somewhat different than those producing for exhibition are producing for a small, breeder market. They value quality birds but tend to opt for what might be termed a more industrial type of bird. They will need eggs in the numbers to acquire and hold regional or even national markets. They may do this by relying on multiple suppliers of the more in-demand breeds. However, do not expect them to make room in the catalog for something very rare, unproven, little-known, or otherwise of limited recognition and value to the general public.

These businesses will need producers with the type of facilities (lighted) that will assure the production of fertile eggs early in the year. A good health program with some type of veterinary monitoring may be required, as well as on-farm inspections by hatchery staff. Also of concern will be a system of handling and shipment to the hatchery that will assure egg quality and hatchability. When we were supplying such eggs we delivered them to a central pickup point about ten miles from home every Saturday afternoon in the local hatching season, mid-February through mid-June.

The closer a flock is located to the hatchery the more desirable it will be to both parties. Supplying a hatchery will not be for everyone, and you will have to be open to having a breed or breeds assigned to you. It may even require birds in greater numbers than what you planned to work with. Do not overextend yourself or your abilities here, as there can be repercussions.

A few fast points on goose care and management are in order to round out this segment:

1. Newly hatched or arrived goslings should be offered lukewarm drinking water.
2. The earlier outlined program for starting ducklings will work with goslings.
3. A 15 percent crude protein ration should be adequate for mature geese.
4. Growth and leg problems can emerge at about two months of age in young geese being fed a layer type ration as a grower. By four weeks of age young geese need to go on a true grower ration with a protein content of up to about 18 percent.
5. Goslings should be fully fledged by four weeks of age.
6. One acre of good grass will carry twenty to forty geese.
7. Geese will generally produce forty-five to seventy eggs during a

laying season. Geese are much more seasonal layers than even ducks or turkeys.

8. For best hatchability goose eggs should be held for no longer than six to ten days.

9. Mrs. Grieve prefers to hatch goose eggs in a cabinet incubator with moving air. She places the eggs on their sides in padded trays to hold them as the trays move.

10. For about the last week of incubation dip each egg in the humidity pan once each day to improve hatchability.

With good nutrition and sanitation geese are among the hardiest and long-lived of all poultry varieties. It is not uncommon to hear of geese being eight to ten years old and still producing fertile eggs in fair numbers.

It has been my experience that with small numbers of geese the market will be very local, and sales will mostly be in small lots. Even if supplying area restaurants, this is just not a bird that is going to appeal to everyone, and the size of the bird mandates that it center a family meal rather than be used frequently for light meals. At our local bird markets goslings typically sell in lots of two to five and go to people that have to be considered one-time customers. They want to develop a pair to raise their own, to be used as feathered watchdogs, to dress up a lake, or to round out their rurban barnyard.

A great many sales will be of just one or two birds at a time. And most will take a bit of a selling job to get top dollar and to address the needs of buyers with very limited experience. As to meat bird sales, going from a goose on foot to a roast goose on the platter will be a major undertaking for most folks and may require some major handholding by the producer. If they botch the cooking of their first high-dollar bird, it is very doubtful they will ever be back to buy another one.

To help consumers through those "I always wanted one of these; now what do I do with it?" moments, a bit of take-along material should be provided. A simple sheet of instructions on how to dispatch, dress, and disjoint a goose will help consumers now embracing the current interest in home butchering and elite processing. It can be accompanied by cooking instructions and a few recipes on what to do with leftovers. And the market might be further expanded by exposing more people to goose on the table.

A friend of ours, a breeder of domestic rabbits, overcame a lot of resistance to eating the "Easter bunny" by taking rabbit-based recipes to every tasting opportunity possible. To emulate his example, you could take goose-based dishes to carry-ins, participate in local food-themed events, donate a goose or two to local fund-raisers, sponsor a trophy for champion goose at the local youth fair, and carve out a niche as the go-to person for goose information at the local farmers' market or bird swap.

Three pairs of geese may be more than enough for the producer to serve a local market. Such markets are built on personal contact between buyer and seller, offering of something unique and perhaps not available from other nearby sources, and the ability of consumers to make purchases at opportune times and amounts.

For optimal production, breeding birds should be replaced after their second or third year of production. Exceptions can certainly be made for top performers or birds of rare or minor breeds, but if you are doing the right kind of job as a breeder you should be producing offspring every bit as good as, and hopefully better than, the birds that produced them. Younger geese have the vigor and agility needed to produce optimum numbers of fertile eggs, and this is a venture to which you must apply a finely sharpened pencil.

It is also a venture that must be undertaken with the fullest possible understanding of the limitations of the species. There will be no three hundred egg–laying geese, nor one hundred and fifty eggers for that matter. Cooking a goose will always be something of a major undertaking for even the most ardent of foodies. I feel safe in saying that there is no Kentucky Fried Goose franchise in the foreseeable future.

I count my goose-related memories among my most precious as a poultry man, but I have to also recognize that their limits will bar them from a fit in our particular poultry yard at this time. I suspect interest in them is going to grow, and the food crowd could fan that fire overnight with but a handful of mentions by a few select chefs and publications.

Geese mature into birds that are bullhorn tough and easy to keep, but they will not fit many small and micro-holdings. You are going to have to really like them to profit from them, and they will require you to work out an extremely detailed plan of production and marketing and then work that plan for all you're worth.

From time to time a swan-related question comes in, and a desire to own a few of these beautiful birds is not uncommon. I had such a desire myself until several years ago, when I read an article about swan keeping in England that said how you could often detect a swan keeper by his missing fingers. It pretty much swept away my aspirations to be a keeper of swans.

The one thousand to three thousand dollar purchase price for a young pair of swans also cooled my ardor for the species. The idea of a Missouri coyote or bobcat having a three-grand swan dinner at my expense was just a tad more of a feast than I cared to finance. Though big and graceful, they are a bird that must be carefully managed and will generally not breed successfully until their third year. They pair bond and will need swimmable water to a depth of at least five feet for successful matings to occur. To encourage reproduction some raisers will create a faux island situated well away from the shore on a larger pond or lake. Swans need a sheltered area for nesting, and to that end plantings are encouraged to better shelter the nesting area. An old tractor tire can serve as a nest base, and it may be sheltered with small bales of hay or straw or a simple lean-to structure. The nesting structure should face to the south, away from prevailing winds, and the birds should be provided with ample amounts of nesting material.

Swans are quite protective of any territory that they consider their own. It is a trait that some are now using to discourage Canada geese from settling in and taking over a small lake or other water system. In the St. Louis area there have been some real problems with Canadas settling in and taking over the water features in business parks and other public areas. They will chase away secretaries and white-collar types that linger during the lunch hour around outside sites.

Into the large nest the female swan, the pen (the male is called a cob), will lay ten or fewer eggs. The male will help to defend the nest, and they will defend it quite aggressively.

They are long-lived birds, and once you have them you will generally have them until they naturally succumb or are taken down by a major predator. Large expanses of swimmable water are an open-housed waterfowl's best defense against predation. As bodies of water freeze over and swimmable areas grow smaller, the birds become more reachable. If this course is to be relied upon, they will need at least a quarter of an acre of open water the year round.

A swan on the water is virtually uncatchable. An old-timer with a small holding in the county to our south had a single black swan that called a large lake there home. The old gentleman passed away, and the bird was offered free to anyone who could catch it. Suffice it to say the bird continuing swimming there gracefully for several years. The young (cygnets) and the birds on land are more easily caught. Grabbing an adult swan is a lot like hand catching a full grown bobcat: the trick isn't in picking it up but rather in putting it back down—safely.

There is a similar question to be answered if your pair does produce a clutch of young. What are you going to do with any surplus birds? With mega-bucks tied up in the seedstock you can't give them away, but you are not very likely to have a clamor of demand for birds with four-figure price tags. There are a handful of waterfowl-themed swaps and auctions across the nation where you will see a few swans, but our local bird market is in its twenty-third year, in a poultry-rich area, and the one thing we have not seen there is a swan.

I have seen pictures and read accounts of swans and peafowl being roasted, placed back into their skins, and served to kings and emperors at royal feasts. An official keeper of the swans is still a part of the Royal Court in England. I'm pretty sure the royal family no longer partakes of swan, but it does bespeak the care they require along with the investment that they can represent. Their best fit in private hands may be in some high-end aviaries and with organizations providing waterway care for business parks and the like.

Wild swans feed on water vegetation, some grass, insects, and some fish spawn. There are a few sources of commercial, pelleted feeds adequate for swans, and they will eat a bit of grain. Waterfowl starter feeds should be offered to the cygnets, and a bit of chopped lettuce and grass can be proffered on the surface of the water.

If taking up something really exotic in the fowl sector, such as swans, seek out a feed supplier with a history of selling animal feeds beyond the norm. Some of the major national companies now provide feeds to zoos and animal parks and have people on staff that can help with some questions relating to the care of more exotic fowl. And the bird staffs at many zoos can be helpful sources of information.

On the water a trio of White Chinese or a couple of pairs of Emden geese would have much the same eye appeal as a bevy of white swans. They are also a more practical species to own and tend, are far more productive, and there should be no reluctance to eat any of their surplus production, even if the king isn't coming over for dinner.

A small number of waterfowl can be kept in the working poultry yard without an investment in water systems beyond a few rubberized pans that are moved often for good sanitation and to prevent mud conditions. A trio or a couple of pairs are often enough to form a waterfowl venture that will serve a local market buying largely from the farmyard.

From such a base of well-bred birds, numbers can grow quickly, but here is a species that the small producer may profit as much or more from increasing quality rather than simply cranking out ever-greater numbers.

Always strive to raise the best that you can before trying to raise the greatest number that you can. And never underestimate the profit potential that can be derived from an exceptional trio of something very distinctively bred, such as a trio of Blue or Chocolate Muscovy ducks or Brown Chinese geese.

In the field of waterfowl production there are some high-profile breeders marketing nationally, but undergirding their sales are the offering and distribution of production data, the how-to of keeping ducks and geese. That information is lacking; it has real cash value itself and adds measurably to the value of birds sold by those who can be the answer man or woman to those getting started with waterfowl. One of the fixtures at our farmers' market is the "duck lady," and her renown is such that she markets to an area of a hundred miles around as well as making numerous sales out of state. She knows her business, that business is ducks, and her phone number is magnet-clipped to ice boxes up and down eastern Missouri.

I repeat, you've got to like, really like, these critters to succeed with them. They are not for everyone and are going to need a lot of promotion. At this moment they may well be, however, that rarest of rare things in traditional livestock production: a ground-floor opportunity.

You just have to answer one question: Does your area need its own "duck lady" or "duck dude"?

CHAPTER 4

The Pigeon
Rollers, Tumblers, and Homers

WILD PIGEON

Once upon a time, few were the farmyards without a dovecote set atop a pole in the farmyard or attached high on the side of an outbuilding. There doves and pigeons lived a near-wild existence, gleaning food from nearby fields and the feed spilt by other residents of the farmyard. The surplus squabs would be harvested shortly before leaving their parents' care and were a staple enjoyed by country folk that later became true gourmet fare.

Pigeons are the domestic descendants of the wild Rock dove, a bird very similar in appearance to the modern blue (gray) street pigeon. Most folks know only of the street pigeon as a creature that many urban souls regard as little more than rats with wings. The common street pigeon—pigeon folks call them "commies"—is a remarkably hardy and adaptable creature. The city birds even have country cousins that live under bridges and around grain elevators.

Some of the very first birds I owned were common pigeons, mostly blue bars and checks, caught from their roosting places in unused buildings nearby. We were always watchful for the occasional red or white bird. However, the muted grays, a color called blue in poultry circles, were by far the most common. The muted hues were nature's way of giving the bird some camouflage when on the roost or in the nest.

Pigeons have been kept and carefully bred for centuries for practical and aesthetic reasons. Charles Darwin kept pigeons to do color breeding experiments as a part of his genetic studies. Their homing instinct was capitalized on early, and they were used to carry messages back to their home base, the home loft.

A pair of pigeons may produce eight to ten young per year and have been developed into a great myriad of breeds. There are breeds weighing but a very few ounces, others weighing three pounds and more. Many are crested or booted. They are bred in a great many different colors and feather patterns, bred for many different competitive sports, and are kept by thousands of people around the world.

The domestic pigeon is divided into three fairly broad categories: ornamentals, athletic or performance birds, and meat birds. Books documenting pigeon breeds run to hundreds of pages. There are simply too many ornamental breeds to list here, and the showroom competition in which they are evaluated for breed type, coloring, and feathering can be quite intense. Indeed many have taken up pigeon keeping to learn more about the art of animal breeding and trait refinement.

The performing bird group includes Homers, Rollers, Tumblers, and a few more. Some Homing pigeons are bred and trained for racing, and those races can vary from distances of under one hundred miles to hundreds of miles. In Europe, Asia, and the Middle East pigeon racing is high sport, and more than one champion bird there has changed hands for five figures to head up a breeding loft. They are also bred in exhibition varieties, including Show Homers and Giant Homers.

Rollers and Tumblers are feathered acrobats. They fly up from a release point—the home loft generally—and dart, swoop, and even tumble or roll downward through the air. A variety called the Parlor Roller actually rolls or somersaults across the ground and is shown in competitions for the longest distance covered in a continuing roll.

Old pigeon hands have a trick they like to play on the unsuspecting souls at our local farmers' market. They will stage a mock argument as if disagreeing over a bird's price to draw the attention of the curious and the greenhorns. The one holding the bird will say loudly, "If that's all it's worth then I'll just pull his head off right now!" He will gently close a hand over the bird's head and drop it to the ground, and it will then begin to roll out through a fast-scattering crowd of onlookers. The bird will soon right itself, the owner will pick it up, and those in the know about such things will have a good laugh.

Some Homers are bred up for size and have been used to produce squabs or brood and raise the young of short-beaked ornamentals that cannot adequately care for hatchlings. Homing pigeons are often used to train bird dogs. They will be positioned around the training field in spring release traps or after being spun and their heads under a wing. Such spun birds will generally hold to cover as the dog nears and comes to a point. The bird will then be flushed and return to the home loft. This practice accustoms the dog to working with live birds in a more controlled environment. They learn to deal with the explosiveness of the flushing birds while both bird and dog are under the control of the handler. The flushed bird returns to the loft and can be used multiple times in the training process.

A growing number of folks are also becoming involved in the "white dove" business. They provide pure white Homing pigeons for funerals, weddings, and other ceremonial events. Two to ten white birds are provided in appropriate white baskets for symbolic release at some point during the ceremony. The bride and groom, for example, might each toss a bird into the air upon emerging from the church. The released birds will rise up, circle to get their bearings, and then set out for their home loft. They symbolize white doves and the meaning mankind has placed on them throughout the ages.

The breeder will bring the birds to the event, position them at the ready, and assist with the release at the appropriate time. Fees for this service vary depending on how far the event is from the home loft and how many birds are desired. A two-bird release within ten miles of home is generally around $50, and a six-bird release within fifty miles of home will run around $150. A ten-bird release is about the top sizewise, and most releases will be within fifty miles of the home loft.

The meat breeds will be our prime focus here and include the King, Texan Pioneer, Carneau, Mondaine, and their crosses. The super large breeds, the Runts and Rumblers, are not good choices for squabbing due to their poor breeding and brooding performance.

The best pigeon for eating is a young bird called a squab. It is harvested from the nest at the time feathers begin to form beneath the wings. They are generally hatched in pairs following an eighteen-day incubation.

Pigeons breed in pairs only. Both parents will incubate the eggs, and both will assist with rearing the young. Pigeons are different from most birds in that they feed their young a regurgitated food termed pigeon's milk. This milky secretion is produced from the lining of the crop and is high in fat, protein, antibodies, and immunity builders. The youngsters take it from their parents' beaks.

They make a free-form nest in a bowl-type container (two should be provided for each pair). Many breeders use a paper nesting bowl that can be discarded after each use for sanitary reasons. Into the nest they will lay two white-shelled eggs about thirty hours apart. The pair of squabs is quite often a male and a female, and the larger, more demonstrative squab is usually the male.

Sexing pigeons is never going to be an easy task. There is generally a bit of a size difference between the two sexes, but I have seen veteran producers stand for many long minutes before a coop of youngsters, sorting and resorting them, and then turn and say they will make no guarantees.

The males tend to be more vocal, their heads and necks may appear to be larger and thicker, they may swell their breasts when courting, and they will push and prod a female (a practice called "driving"). The pelvic bones at the aft of the body can be helpful in sexing as the birds mature. In females there should be a larger gap between the tip ends of these two bones to allow for egg laying. The Texan Pioneer was developed to be an auto- or self-sexing bird. The males and females develop in different colors. This breed was also developed for larger size and growth to be used as a squabbing breed.

Sometimes the pair will build another nest and produce another clutch of eggs while still tending young in the first nest. Young may even flutter from the nest to the floor of the loft where the parents will still tend to them until they are able to care for themselves. Other adults in the pen may savage these youngsters, however, resulting in death or injury. Head damage thus inflicted to young pigeons is sometimes referred to as "scalping." Young pigeons are called "squeakers" due to the nature of their vocalizations. Some breeds are far more aggressive with each other than others. The Modena is one that comes quickly to mind, and they can be especially territorial around the nest.

It is best to remove young birds to a separate loft when they are eating on their own. Some will leave them there until they form pairs on their own. Others will select the birds they wish to have mated and place them in a small coopage to form what is a called a "forced mating." Pairs bond tightly, and forced matings will be a must with older birds that have lost a mate or to re-pair birds that are not producing to the desired performance.

Squab is a dark meat; essentially, a serving of squab is just the breast meat of the young bird. A well-bred squab will produce a dressed weight of several ounces, and one such bird typically forms a single serving.

Squab is one of those meat items everyone has heard of, that most associate with the good life, and with which very few people have had any actual experience. I know of many pigeon hobbyists that do not even eat squab. On the other hand, back in those days when there was a dovecote in every farmyard, pigeon was nearly a diet staple, eaten in many forms, including pigeon pie. Those birds lived a largely catch-as-catch-can existence, foraging for nearly every bite of their food. Grain blends and mixes still form a large component of pigeon feeds. There are commercially available rations that are elaborate blends of grains and legumes, including feedstuffs such as maple peas.

I noted earlier that pigeons were one of the first varieties of bird that I kept, and pigeon keeping has been a youthful pursuit of a great many. Many of those have sought a way to turn that youthful passion into a profitable economic pursuit.

As a writer, the letters and calls from readers that I remember the most are the ones that took me to task. Fortunately, there haven't been a great many of those, but one that sticks in my memory came many years ago after I had written a short article about pigeon keeping as a possible small venture. That writer had at me for holding out a bit of hope, what he felt was false hope, that something more could be made from a modest flock of pigeons. I didn't promise riches with them, but there are some practical roots to pigeon keeping, and few are our local poultry markets at which a few pairs of pigeons change hands. Good pairs sell locally for ten to thirty dollars depending upon their breed.

Over the years I have kept many breeds, from Turbits and Croppers to Rollers and Homers to Texan Pioneers and Kings. I like a bird that feels solid in the hand and have a particular fondness for white-feathered birds. We have just added a small set of White Homers.

For meat production the birds need to be large, but not so large as to have problems with reproduction, brooding, and squab care. Some birds bred for exhibition are simply too large and have not been selectively bred for the traits essential to efficient and economic levels of squab production.

The bird that most now associate with squab production is the White King. To be exact, it should be termed the Utility King. It is a hardy bird, matures quickly, and, as a white-feathered bird, will have cleaner dressing qualities. Crossbreeding can be done with some squabbing stock, but with such a niche market product as the squab pure breeding will be just one more step to establishing any sort of a "brand" presence.

The challenge with squab production will be to find a consistent market, one that will take birds in any sort of number, and one that will pay a good price for what has to be marketed as a truly premium nature food item. The literature gives many accounts of squabbing pairs with the ability to produce ten squabs per year, five clutches of two squabs each.

Let's talk numbers here for a minute. You think ten squabs, a good-sized family might eat that many in a single Sunday night supper. Ten pair is a modest number of pairs to keep, but in another year we're up to one hundred squabs. Did I mention that that good-sized family has probably never eaten squab? That those ten pairs might give you twenty squabs at a time to market? Where do you even go for price discovery of any sort?

Pigeons can be quite productive creatures. Even in a simple loft setup with temperatures that vary with the season, a good pair may produce six to eight young yearly. And you can't store their production on a back shelf waiting for a market to emerge. A squab is a squab for only a short time.

Where they have been produced in any number, squabs have generally been direct marketed to consumers, usually straight into the restaurant trade. That market is again opening to independent producers due to the fast-growing farm-to-fork movement. Still, producers are going to have to meet the chef at the kitchen door or find someone to broker sales into that market.

One of our old twelve-foot-by-sixteen-foot chicken houses could be quickly rehabbed to house and produce a great many pigeons. The task of getting that production moved out of the building and off the farm would be greater than any other, however.

Now I wish I could tell you there is some secret to all of this that makes it all fall together easily, but there isn't. This is going to take a lot of what the books on salesmanship call cold calls and shoe-leather wear. In many cities now you will find local groups of Slow Foods people and kindred spirits. They may be able to help with your marketing efforts. An interest in pigeon such as what arose for heirloom chicken and rabbit breeds may occur. There are live bird markets to be found around several major cities such as Chicago and Miami. And there are beginning to emerge some brokers of naturally produced farm products with access to the restaurant trade and specialty markets. You may have some luck finding all of these by placing a phone call to the staff of the weekly food section of the nearest major urban newspaper. The producer is going to have to really put himself out there to get this kind of production profitably marketed. It will involve a great deal of one-to-one interaction. Contact might be made with a CSA producer or a producer seeking to broaden his market and/or market year with the inclusion of specialty meat items.

Local producers in our area took matters into their own hands and organized and ran their own monthly bird market from February through November. The officers are constantly reaching out to buyers, or end consumers, or volume buyers for items such as surplus cockerels that are produced each hatching season.

Buyers for such an elite product are going to have to be stroked a bit, and there will be a big job of consumer education. Jacques Pépin may know a thousand things to do with a squab, but Sam and Susie Suburbia will have just one bad experience with the pricey little birds and never buy them again.

By the numbers now, I would say buy two or three pairs of well-bred birds; good ones may be closer to you than you think and for less that the prices you see in some of the catalogs now. Even before the birds, invest in a couple of good books on pigeon care.

We have a simple, all-wire aviary of three feet by four feet by six feet tucked away in one multi-use poultry building that handily holds a couple pairs of pigeons that we bought second-hand for a very few dollars. We use it for overflow, but it would be a good learner's coop.

With but very few exceptions, these are quite hardy and adaptable birds. Their feral cousins survive under bridges and along building ledges in the heat of New York City summers and the chill of Chicago winters.

I have seen pigeon lofts built on a par with royal palaces and pigeons performing quite well in refitted chicken houses and older mobile homes. If converting housing from one species to another, it should be very thoroughly cleaned and the floors and surfaces scraped. The unit should then be disinfected, open as much as possible to sunshine and fresh air, and left vacant for at least thirty days. The longer it can stand idle, the greater the likelihood of breaking the life cycle of parasites and disease-causing organisms. Six months would be just about perfect.

A space four feet deep by three feet wide by four feet high is held to be quite adequate for the needs of two pairs of medium-sized pigeons, possibly three pairs in a pinch. They should never be crowded, and only mated pairs should be kept in the breeding loft. Singles, especially odd males, can create real problems in the breeding loft, and weaned youngsters are best moved to a loft of their own.

Pigeon numbers can build quickly, and just because you have an empty barn on the back of the place doesn't mean you should endeavor to fill it with pigeons. Quite honestly, what makes any livestock venture more vulnerable to disease is overcrowding, stress, and the presence of great numbers of breeding stock worn down by the care of young.

Yes, to be truly profitable your birds have to be kept in production, but in an orderly manner, with carefully planned matings, in a facility that keeps them safe and comfortable, and supported with high levels of nutrition. If your market and your facilities are such that ten pairs meet the demand and are well-tended, then why crowd them just to say that you then have X number of birds? X number of anything seldom performs up to needs or expectations.

At a distance, our four-pair breeding loft could be mistaken for a privy with a rabbit hutch attached to the east side by wood screws and fender washers. Pretty it is not, but it is serviceable, we can tend it while standing fully erect (something I really appreciate since reaching my rusty golden years), and the birds are nearly always within arm's reach.

Would I add more birds? A hesitant yes, if I could sell more birds. Sadly, a lot of pigeon folks consider themselves bird poor. They have larger numbers than they feel they really need.

Pigeons are very interesting birds with which to work. Unlike just about any other bird species, doves and pigeons lap their drinking water rather than sip or dip it. They will appreciate bathing in a large pan of drinking water two or three times each week. They are very temperature tolerant. I have read many accounts of producers to the Canadian border providing no supplemental winter heating and even getting some squab production in the cold months. And a good loft will provide four square feet of floor space for each breeding pair. Thus an older, twelve-foot-by-sixteen-foot poultry house, fairly typical for our part of the Midwest, might well shelter up to fifty pair of breeding pigeons. With that number you should be pushing the thousand squabs a year mark. And with those numbers you had best either like pigeon on the plate or be one heck of a squab marketer.

The loft should be draft-free, the interior wall painted white for improved winter lighting, and the structure kept scrupulously free of vermin. Dust from feathers and feed particles can be a real problem with pigeons, sometimes causing a human health problem termed "pigeon lung." Some raisers will wear a mask coving the mouth and nose when working in the loft for any extended length of time. Once diagnosed with this problem, most will leave behind pigeon keeping and may even have similar problems with other sources of dust and rabbit dander. Although a risk, lung problems for bird keepers are relatively rare. I had a classmate in grade school that developed respiratory problems that caused him to miss many weeks of school. His family owned a feed mill, and he spent a great deal of time there. There were a few feral pigeons present, but there was also much grain dust and large particulate matter present in the air. His problems were very real, but no others in his family were affected, and they owned and operated that facility for decades.

Many pigeon lofts now are refitted garden sheds or even store-bought units of fancily painted woods and metal. They are elevated on legs three to four feet in length and are often sold knocked down or in kit form. They typically have solid wooden floors. Such solid floors are then covered with a layer of sand or ground corn cobs. Straw, even chopped straw, is a poor choice as it can become matted down and hold in moisture.

The sand or cobs can be raked to remove wastes, wet spots can be lifted up and out with a shovel, and the floor covering should be removed and replaced twice a year. Spring and floor poultry house and loft cleaning are traditional practices throughout much of the country.

Many spins have been placed on loft floor management over the years.

Some would even keep a couple of the calmer "floor" bantams, in the loft to keep the floor litter stirred and to clean up any spilt feed. They have to be selected for a gentle nature to not pursue any birds that light in their area or any youngsters that settle to the loft floor.

Heavy-gauge wire flooring, aviary wire, is deemed by many to be the near ideal flooring material choice. Nearly ideal and very, very expensive. Such mesh can withstand human foot traffic if laid down on floor joists on sixteen-inch centers. Wastes fall through onto the next level, which is fully enclosed to prevent drafts from coming up through the floor and vermin access. Into this space some will introduce a few chickens to clean up any spilt feedstuffs.

An eight-foot-by-twelve-foot building will accommodate up to twenty-five pairs of birds. Larger units can be segmented to hold breeders and birds of different ages in smaller groups. Those propagating a breed for exhibition and some sales of seedstock seem to find a level of comfort and satisfaction with the keeping of eight to twelve pairs of superior-bred birds.

Pigeon loft furnishings will differ a bit from those used in the hen house. A holdover from their Rock dove ancestry, pigeons like to roost high and will seek recesses and darker corners in which to nest. Simple, inverted V roosts made from short pieces of wood can be screwed into loft walls for pigeon roost points.

Monitor all roosting points often for potential sources of drafts. One-eyed colds and simple respiratory problems can often be corrected simply by finding and eliminating sources of drafts around the roosting points.

Nest boxes are generally twelve inches by twelve inches by twelve inches to twelve by fourteen by sixteen inches depending on the size of the breed being kept. Two such boxes, side by side, should be provided for each pair where production is being pushed. Not long ago a metal nest unit made with the smaller segments intended for Leghorn hens showed up at one of our bird markets. The small sections were a real deterrent to our producers with the larger brown egg–laying heritage chicken breeds. It did light up our pigeon-keeping members and quickly went home with one of them. The pigeon supply houses offer many different types of pigeon nests, and many of them come with fronts made from doweling. They are double-nest units, and the sliding fronts can be latched closed.

Sliding door fronts can even be bought separately to attach to existing nest boxes. The closing fronts can then make of nest boxes breeding units for forced matings. The selected male and female, cock and hen, can be held there until the pair bond is formed. Then the door can be opened and/or the front removed. They may have to be so contained for some time and fed and watered in the contained area. These units should be cleaned and scraped often and monitored closely for the presence of vermin.

Nest bowls should be placed into the nest. These are bowl-like structures into which the two eggs are laid, incubated, and the squabs brooded and tended by their parents. Once upon a time they were actually made of a clay material and could be cleaned and used repeatedly. Most often used now are paper pulp bowls that can be used once and then disposed of in a natural way.

Pigeon feeding and watering equipment often has a metal, cone-shaped top to discourage the birds from alighting atop them. This is done to prevent contamination of the contents with fecal material. They often have a shrouded opening that requires the birds to reach in to get feed or water to help prevent them from slinging about any feed or water.

The pigeon bath can be a simple, low-sided pan. The three-gallon black rubber models available from most farm supply stores are a good choice for this. They are durable, easy to clean, will suffer no freeze damage, and are quite inexpensive. I have even used some of the smallest of these containers as nest bowls.

Most of the major livestock feed companies now offer at least a short line of pigeon feed products. They may be special order items in some parts of the country, but a great many feed suppliers are now expanding their feed lines to supply the growing number of artisanal livestock producers. Most often seen will be a pelleted ration, generally what is termed a mini-pellet, much smaller than the pellets meant for feeding hoofed stock. These rations are complete feeds providing all of the nutrients needed for breeding and developing birds. Some offer complex grain and legume mixes that are favored by some veteran producers, a few of which have tried to form their own mixes based on locally grown grains. The addition of certain legumes such as maple peas is critical to developing fully balanced, all-grain rations.

A lot of grain sorghum (milo) is fed to pigeons here in the Midwest. With grains in the ration pigeons have to be supplied with appropriate-sized grit to facilitate digestion. I like to offer cherry or red granite grit, and a small bag will last quite a while. With modest numbers of pigeons, the costs in most regions should favor the feeding of pelleted, complete rations. There is generally much less waste with feeding pelleted products to poultry. The heat and pressure of the pelleting process also tends to free up more of the nutrients in the feedstuffs.

Poultry folks, regardless of their species of choice, are always tweaking their rations and trying new things. I enjoy sitting back and listening to the old hands talk, and I have learned much from them. I had often heard of the practice of feeding a certain brand of baby chick starter/grower to pigeons with good results. It is not a cheap product, but it's much less costly than many special feeds for pigeons. I have been trying it for a short time with quite good results. It keeps the eggs full and the hens on the nest. I will be trialing it for a good while longer, but the youngsters grow well on it, too.

The birds clearly enjoy having water to bathe in, and one old hen bird here seems resolved to endure Missouri summers by remaining in a constant wet state. I recommend adding two milliliters of injectable Ivermectin to each gallon of bath water. It will help control external parasites such as mites, and some birds may even drink enough of the water to help with the control of internal parasites.

An insect pest arrived in our area a few years ago when the Mississippi was in spring flood stage: the buffalo or turkey gnat. It is a nasty little creature that swarms and bites, and on some people its bites can raise quite large welts. Its behavior can be especially stressful to poultry, and it always arrives here at that time of the spring when many birds are closely penned in breeding groups. They swarm the face and head, enter nostrils, and are compounded by early rounds of humid spring heat. They have caused substantial death losses on some farms and young stock and females on the nest are most vulnerable to these pests. They have a tendency not to enter too deeply into darkened buildings, but birds in shaded coops and on sundecks can be quite vulnerable. Producers in our area lost many squabs still in the nest this spring, perhaps because many were lulled into a false sense of security because there was little or no gnat presence the previous year due to hot and dry conditions.

The gnat's life cycle is brief, but there have been two-hatch years here. Depending on the weather, they can make for a rather trying two weeks to a month in the poultry yard. There are a few ways to minimize the effects of these pests. Vanilla extract can be mixed into a heavy solution with water and misted onto the birds. During heavy onslaughts many raisers will wet a soft cloth with the vanilla extract and water solution and wipe down the birds, paying special attention to the head and face area. The mixture should also be sprayed on the exterior surfaces in the poultry yard and should be applied three or four times each day. The vanilla extract varieties available in Mexican food specialty stores seem to be the best for this use. Stable sprays containing pyrethrins and citronella can also be applied to coop surfaces several times each day to help repel the pests. A strong smell seems to be one of the essentials to a successful repellent for them. Some springs of late have found our poultry yard smelling like a bakery or a citrus grove.

Drinking water should be kept clean and available to the birds at all times. The water should be changed at least once each day and two or more times a day during periods of hot weather or in the winter when it will freeze after only a short time in an unheated situation. It is crucial that birds feeding young have a steady supply of quality drinking water.

At about six months of age pigeons will begin pairing efforts and can produce squabs at every season of the year. Breeding for elaborate coloring or feathering has seemed to affect the reproductive performance of many lines now. The producer taking up pigeons for squab production will, I believe, have to embark on an extensive period of selective breeding for better reproduction and productive type.

We recently added some pigeon pairs back to our poultry yard: a few pairs of white Homers to develop a squabbing line and a vividly colored pair of Indian Fantails because, well, they caught my eye and I think they're pretty. My wife, Phyllis, describes my loft as being of the "outhouse school" of architecture. It was built for very little cost with bits and pieces of material we had around the place, and we will be largely about flock building and type shaping for a long time to come. They will never be a large venture for us, but a bit of interest in squab production has arisen in our area, and, frankly, I missed having a few pigeons. I find their cooing a quite pleasing sound.

Squabbing has always been a big business only in areas with close access to large populations having some experience with and appreciation for squab as fancy table fare. As a result, most of the large squab farms were found on the East and West Coasts. The term once used to describe smallholdings adjacent to urban areas where poultry were held in large numbers was "plants." In the 1940s and 1950s there were layer, broiler, and squab plants adjacent to many urban centers on the East Coast and California. The Los Angeles County area was home to many facilities that were a couple of acres in size and home to two to four thousand laying hens or several hundred pairs of pigeons. In New York City you will still encounter numerous rooftop lofts that are home to modest flocks of performing and exhibition pigeons.

Where pigeons are held in large numbers the workload can be quite substantial, and they are not inexpensive birds to feed. Loft management should be to such detail that the performance of each breeding pair is fully monitored and documented in venture records. Keep in mind some of the larger breeds do tend to be a bit more aggressive with each other.

In this section I should probably note the events of a few years ago here in the Midwest. The hog business had just been turned upside down by a huge drop in prices, and a lot of small, independent producers were left with hog housing with very few other potential uses. A firm, called Pigeon King International, emerged on the scene promoting pigeon production in refitted hog buildings, other barns, and older mobile homes. They would supply the breeding stock and assist with the marketing of squabs to China. It was a slick operation with glossy pamphlets and smooth presentations at a number of different farm events. They were selling breeder birds for fifty dollars a pair in lots of fifty pairs and were encouraging producers to begin with at least two hundred fifty pairs.

I chanced upon one of their booths at a farm show and took a look at the breeding stock they had on display, including one pair of smallish flying Homers, a rather colorful pair of Rollers, and one of the better pairs of Tipplers I had seen in a long time. At the time, good pairs of those first two breeds were bringing ten to twenty dollars at our local market as proven breeders, and the Roller and Tippler were never squabbing breeds. They were touting the sale of meat squabs at double figure prices into an Asian country where workers had to toil for many years just to buy a bicycle. They especially targeted Amish and Mennonite farmers, knowing, as hindsight revealed, that these groups would not take legal action against them as this little scheme began to unwind.

As the first squabs approached market age, the markets weren't there, and suddenly the promoters of all of this weren't either. Pigeons were abandoned, lofts simply thrown open, much money was lost, and good pigeon men and women struggled through some very hard times as the birds were so steeply discounted. For a long time, anything to do with pigeons was viewed with great suspicion. Arlan Galbraith, the man allegedly behind the scheme, was arrested in 2010 and charged with defrauding investors of more than $1 million.

Some of the ill feeling this scam engendered is only just now going away, but it still hovers in the back of the minds of nearly all U.S. poultry raisers as we view and assess this modern poultry renaissance.

Small farmers are always questing for new enterprises to add to their farm venture mix. Those that meet the needed criteria—small space requirements, simple housing needs, and modest start-up and operating costs—are all rare. It was this sort of appeal that drew so many to the previously noted pigeon production scam.

Many pigeon fanciers have tried to turn their passion for these birds into a business pursuit only to be brought up short. Squab falters as a staple in the U.S. diet for many of the same reasons that rabbit has. It is a rich, dark meat with which few are familiar; it has a pricey and near-exotic image; it comes from very young, not easily transportable birds; and many would-be consumers carry a negative image of the meat based on street pigeons.

It would be hard to think of a species of livestock much smaller than the pigeon, but livestock they are and so they must be managed. To be profitable they must be kept in production, meaning they must be well tended and well fed.

At fourteen to twenty-one days after hatching a brace of squabs, the hen may lay a second clutch of eggs into a nest next to her current one. Eggs will be laid a day or so apart; she will then begin the incubation process and leave the male to finish the task of rearing the older squabs. A breeding pair at a high level of productivity will consume ninety to one hundred pounds of a good ration yearly.

Most pigeon rations are now bought as pelleted, complete feeds or grain and legume mixes to be fed in whole form. They are generally sold in fifty-pound sacks, and a hundred pounds of a good pigeon feed now can take a mighty big bite out of a fifty-dollar bill. I have a hobby of collecting old agriculture texts, and one of them revealed the following formulation for a feed mixture for pigeons: thirty-five pounds of yellow corn, twenty pounds of milo or grain sorghum (called kafir in some old texts), twenty pounds of cowpeas, fifteen pounds of hard red wheat, five pounds of oat groats, and five pounds of hempseed. Good luck finding some of those ingredients at your local feed store now. Those older and all-grain rations were meant to be fed with added mineral supplementation. Again, from an older text comes this formulation for a pigeon mineral mix: forty pounds of medium crushed oyster shell, thirty-five pounds of limestone or granite grit, ten pounds of medium-sized hardwood charcoal, five pounds of ground bone, five pounds of ground limestone, four pounds of salt, and one pound of Venetian red. Here again we see items that can no longer be pulled down from feed store shelves.

Many will opt for white-feathered varieties due to their cleaner dressing qualities. And, alas, good candidates for a squabbing flock will not be easily or inexpensively assembled. Adult pigeons can be shipped through the U.S. mail. It will take time to assemble even a small squabbing flock, and most will probably be based on a single, pure breed. This can be an advantage in the marketing of squabs; however King, Carneau, and Mondain breeds have a long association with squabbling and a name recognition that can carry it through to the marketplace.

While old, wooden, thirty-dozen egg cases were once used for pigeon nests, the times have changed, and to get premium prices a farm product must be produced in a premium manner. It will be difficult to sell squabs to a local restaurant if you supply them two birds one week, ten the next, and then none for a month.

As I noted early on, it has been the hope of just about every boy and girl who grew up keeping pigeons to eventually make some sort of "business" out of them. It has happened for only a very few.

A father and son, very early cooperators in our local farmers' market, bring numerous breeds of pigeon to the market as a part of their poultry offering. They have one of the largest systems of lofts in our part of the state, travel extensively with their birds, and keep numerous breeds and varieties. They are the "pigeon guys," and it is their expertise and willingness to share it that draws buyers to them.

They raise some Frillbacks and American Fantails, breeds that some would consider hobbyist breeds. The birds are very well-bred, and their coloring and feathering do draw the eye. These birds they sell to 4-Hers as project birds, to other breeders, and to those rurban folks who want some avian pizzazz for their "place in the country." They produce some good Homers and Rollers that are sold largely to other "pigeon flyers." Folks keep such birds for racing and flying competitions, as well as the challenge of producing good, feathered athletes. Some of these birds they also sell to hunting dog trainers to help develop bird-finding and flushing skills in young bird dogs. Such birds return to their home loft when flushed. This father-and-son pair has also begun developing a line of squabbing birds by breeding a line of Kings and a line of Carneau. The father nearly always has a handful of another breed or two with which he is experimenting or trialing in our eastern Missouri climes. Fantails strutting in their cages and Parlor Rollers set to tumbling on the market grounds draw buyers to their market display, and the duo always seems happiest when they send a boy or girl home with their first pair of pigeons, generally sold to them for but a very few dollars.

The rural scene has gone from a time when no farmyard would be considered complete without a dovecote of its own to the point where many farmers consider the occasional strayed Homer or feral pigeon little more than a rat with wings. A few times over the years we have had farmers of the industrial school pass through our bird market and they stand almost dumbfounded before the varied pigeon breeds displayed there. They say they didn't know that pigeons could look like that, but I think they just didn't know pigeons.

The local and artisanal food movements are reviving interest in all sorts of classical and traditional food items, and squab may be something that will benefit from this. It still has some name recognition and is regarded as a true, upscale food item.

A few years ago about the only one eating pigeon around here was the fellow hired to trap the feral birds around local grain elevators. Again, however, they are starting to have some haute and exotic appeal. There is a big-selling job ahead with them, along with a real task of assembling and breeding up the genetics needed to create a truly productive flock of birds.

A producer now selling broilers or waterfowl into the restaurant trade might be in a better position to generate interest in and the sale of local, farm-fresh squab. There is a pretty good supporting infrastructure in place for pigeon producers. There are strong breeder clubs for many of the breeds in place and several major firms supplying health care supplies, books, and loft equipment. In point of fact, many health care products developed for pigeons have been adapted for use with other poultry species.

I know people who have kept pigeons for decades and never eaten a single squab. I have taken them up and set them aside too many times in my life. And there are those who have taken the lessons they have learned in color and type breeding with pigeons and applied them to other, more economically prominent livestock varieties. The pigeon will, I believe, always be a poultry variety of fringe stratus. They are of great value to those who keep them, even those with just a pair or two as a remembrance of a long-ago, youthful passion. It is often said that a boy who loved pigeons or other fowl will set them aside once he discovers the charms of girls; however, the female companion he chooses will eventually have to make room in her life for his return to that earlier love.

Challenges to modern pigeon production will include finding an enduring market, doing the price finding needed to satisfy both producer and consumer, developing a profitable producing flock, and continually promoting the merits of the bird. And any producer must like them and value them for the graceful and endearing creatures that God made them.

CHAPTER 5

The Guinea
Poultry to Ponder

GUINEA

A poultry variety even more exotic in nature than the pigeon is the guinea. It is a bird virtually unchanged from its wild forebears still found on the plains of Africa. Many will tell you that they really don't own guineas; they just provide them with some room to roam and a bit of feed and shelter when the snow flies.

The guinea is the bird that Hemingway shot for the camp table when on safari in Africa. Fried young guinea is a regional favorite of the Midwest, seen in late summer and fall when the keets of the year have reached pan size. Guinea is all dark meat of a very rich flavor, and it's seen on the table very rarely and then only in high-end restaurants. It is a culinary favorite in France, where poultry in great variety is one of the pillars of classic French cuisine.

A few years ago a daytime TV celebrity with an estate home in a state with a history of Lyme disease cases spoke several times of using guineas on her large holding as a natural control measure for ticks. They have a long history of eating ticks and in rural Missouri are said to repel snakes and keep even the fearsome chigger at bay. They also have a well-deserved reputation as feathered watchdogs. They raise a true din when anything intrudes into their territory. If kept in large enough numbers they have even been said to deter winged predators such as hawks.

Their near-wild nature and the propensity to roost in trees make them vulnerable to that winged predator of the night, the owl. An owl will alight next to a guinea roosting on a limb, crowd it off its roosting point, and, as it flutters groundward in the dark, will dive and snatch it away. For those of you who have held on to a relic of your disco-era ways and have a strobe light up in the attic or bought one at a yard sale, it can be given a second life positioned in a poultry yard above the pens and coops. It is said that an owl will not fly through a strobe light.

Guineas have been domesticated for over four thousand years, and here I use "domesticated" in the broadest sense of the word. They were kept and valued for the delicate and rich flavor of their flesh, which is all dark meat. The proper name for them is Helmeted guinea fowl, but it seems a bit high-falutin' for a bird that has carved out a rather catch-as-catch-can existence on the small farms of the United States.

For much of my life guineas were to be found almost exclusively in Pearl, White, and a Splash blend of the two. From time to time you would see a few of the Lavender variety, but guinea breeding was left to the whims of nature, much like the weather and the arrival of the cicadas in summer. They were not a cultivated crop. The Pearl variety of guinea, gray with small white spots, is nearly identical to its wild counterparts.

Mating Pearl or Lavender birds with White guineas will produce the so-called Splash birds. They will have the Pearl or Lavender patterns with large splotches of white on the breast and across the wings. There is some resistance to the White variety as many believe that the color makes those birds more vulnerable to predator attack. The guinea is bred in several other colors and patterns, including the Chocolate, Buff Dundotte, Lavender, Violet, Coral Blue, Regal Purple, Slate, Splash, and more. They are all color phases of the same bird.

A more recent development has been a bird termed the Jumbo, French Jumbo, or French variety. They have been developed to be a larger and meatier bird than the typical guinea seen on U.S. farms and smallholdings. They will have a mature weigh of one to two pounds heavier than the standard guinea fowl. One or two pounds larger would not matter much with steers or even wethers, but the standard guinea male or cock has a mature weight of four pounds and the female or hen an adult weight of three and a half pounds.

I have a friend, an old poultry hand from northern Missouri, who says that he predicted forty years ago that the guinea would be taken up seriously by the American Poultry Association, that it would be bred in greater variety, and even be entered into competition in poultry shows. All of this and more has come to pass. Guinea meat, however, is still not widely eaten. More people probably value the bird as a natural means of insect control or as an alarm system in the poultry yard. Ranging fowl of numerous species will hunker down when guineas sound the alarm. And a great many producers keep them because having a few guineas was just one more thing you did as a part of farm-keeping in the forties and fifties, times when a lot of us in the Boomer generation were foaled.

Guineas are fairly hardy birds once feathered out and will winter well even here in northeastern Missouri where winter temperatures often fall below zero, well below zero. During cold times they do need to be held in dry, draft-free housing, and they will do best when fed a game bird ration appropriate to their stage of development or reproduction. They are seasonal in their breeding and laying patterns and are bad to steal out their nests if allowed even half a chance to do so. They are staunch to the nest and after a twenty-eight-day incubation period will hatch off fair numbers of keets from a clutch of eggs that can number up to twenty. Alas, they are, originally, birds of the dry African veldt, and their little keets don't fare well in the dewy mornings and thundering downpours of midwestern springs and early summers. And the hen, her eggs, and young are all very vulnerable to a great many different predators when on the nest.

As with the spring hunts here for morel mushrooms, many with guineas spend a deal of time ferreting out nest sites. The plan is to scoop up the young keets as quickly as possible when they emerge from the egg and then brood them artificially. Survival rates there tend to be much greater than even when keets are brooded and reared under much tamer chicken hens.

The preferred method is to brood and rear guinea keets with a few baby chicks. They tend to have a calming and a gentling effect on the little keets. If raised and then kept with these brooder mates they will be more tractable, more easily contained, and will be more comfortable in and return regularly to nighttime housing.

If they can be shut into secure housing each night and not released until late each morning they will be more apt to lay in nests inside the housing unit. The eggs are more easily collected, better egg quality can be maintained, the hatching dates are predictable, hatching rates will increase, and more keets will be saved.

Incubating guinea eggs artificially requires a bit of care and a plan of management in the incubator. First there is that twenty-eight-day incubation period. The eggs have to be removed from the egg turner on the twenty-fifth day and laid down to hatch. Guinea eggs have one of the thickest shells of any domestic fowl, and unit humidity must be managed accordingly. The eggs can be very difficult to candle clearly due to this thickness, and newly emerged keets are among the most vigorous of all hatchlings.

Against my better judgment an acquaintance once talked me into hatching sixty of his guinea eggs in the cabinet incubator that we had at the time. It was an incubator with a cabinet that was deeper than my arms were long. He assured me that the eggs were absolutely fresh, had had no incubation, and that the keets would all hatch together. On the tenth day of incubation little keets began popping up in the farthest corners of the incubator, and it took long minutes with the incubator door open to extract them from those far nooks.

If left on their own guineas will tend to pair up, and the male will stay close to the hen when she is on the nest. A couple of hens may merge their clutches of hatchlings into the larger flock for added protection. In more controlled situations a male needs to be provided with three to four hens to assure fertile eggs. Here a female guinea is termed a hen and a male a rooster.

Though larger in size guineas are essentially game birds. Game bird starter is the best choice for a ration to start and grow the young keets. The small particle size and nutrient density of those rations are needed by the smaller sized keets to grow better and be healthier as they develop. In cold weather the birds will need to be offered at least a simple grain mixture twice a day—maybe three times in severe weather. Typically this will be a mixture of corn, wheat, and oats. We generally offered our guineas the same rations our chickens received, a laying ration in pelleted form. A bit of scratch grain will boost energy levels and may be used to draw the birds into an enclosed roosting area each evening. Egg production may be increased by feeding a higher protein content, game bird breeders ration.

Old hands would also offer grit, oyster shell, and even a bit of charcoal on a free-choice basis. Many modern complete feeds now eliminate the need to offer supplemental grit. It is certainly a hot button issue, but the nature of these birds is such that they will benefit from some animal-sourced protein in their feed. At one time this might have been done by offering some farm-produced skimmed milk, and now it might be done by offering a bit of pet food or catfish food.

All fowl will savor and benefit from being fed a bit of green feed such as cabbage, kale, collards, or even green, leafy legume hay. Do not leave it on the ground, however, as it will soon be trodden into a sodden mess on the pen or house floor. Suspend greens just above the birds' heads, and they will benefit both nutritionally and mentally from the stimulation of pecking and reaching for them.

In starting with guineas, keets are probably the best option in most instances. When raised up with a few baby chicks they will better imprint on the home farmyard and hold close to it when they mature.

A number of years ago a lady came to our farmers' market several times one spring and early summer and always bought a half-dozen or so adult guineas. Her purchases were certainly appreciated, but she was purchasing far too many guineas to be of practical use in our area. I asked her about it and she replied that she was hoping to establish a small guinea flock on her little piece of rural Missouri. It was a reasonable goal, but I had to ask why she was purchasing so many birds? She answered that each Saturday she took her purchases home, set them down in her little farmyard, and, within a day or two, they would all be gone.

The simple truth is that few birds are more difficult to relocate than adult guineas. Adult birds should be closely penned for thirty to sixty days after being moved and even then may not imprint on their new home. It is in them to range about widely, and if turned out directly into strange territory they will all too often wander straight away. Often they will gravitate to other farms nearby with guineas or other poultry.

When bought from hatcheries little guineas are typically sold in lots of no less than thirty keets to assure that they have a safe and warm ride through the U.S. mail. Where there will be no extended time in transit they may be shipped in smaller lots or perhaps blended with hatchlings of another species of similar size. Depending on variety, guinea keets now sell for four to seven dollars each, and hatching eggs may run thirty to fifty dollars per dozen plus shipping.

Hatching eggs of most poultry species would appear to be an inexpensive way to enter a poultry venture, but allow me to quote an old exercise I found in a book of grammar, "Never endeavor to enumerate your juvenile fowl prior to their emergence from their calciferous containment." In Missouri plain speak, don't count your chickens before they hatch.

Hatching eggs fare very poorly in transit, and the eggs that break will stain and impair the hatchability of the eggs around them. Packaging for hatching eggs has gotten better in recent times, but shipping boxes that cushion each egg in a mini-foam nest are expensive and will not fully protect the eggs from rough handling. Labeling a box "Hatching Eggs" almost seems to invite rough handling and temperature extremes. And postal insurance does not always cover the full costs of hatching eggs. An old Missouri hand would buy a cheap wine glass from a big box store and add it to each shipment of hatching eggs. He would label the box "Fragile: Glass" and insure it for five hundred dollars, actually paying very little to do so. Handling rough enough to break or hurt the eggs would break the glass, and the broken glass made the case for his insurance claim.

Under the best of circumstances a hatching rate of 35–40 percent is considered quite good with shipped eggs, and I have known of producers that drove many hours just to personally handle and transport hatching eggs. Transported hatching eggs, whether driven ten miles down the road or mailed over several states, should upon arrival stand for twenty-four hours before being placed into the incubator. This will allow them to settle back and the air cells to properly position. The shells should be cleaned of any staining that has resulted from eggs broken in transit. They should also be candled for any fine cracks or other shell damage that could result in egg spoilage during incubation. Dried egg can be removed with a light sanding, but any damaged or badly stained eggs should be discarded.

Keets are generally sold as-hatched or incubator-run. It will be a safe bet that there will be a preponderance of males to females. If bought in very small lots, numbers will often skew badly toward one sex over another. Many believe that guinea sex can be determined by the size of the fleshy growth at the top of the head, the helmet, and the wattles. Their reasoning is the larger those fleshy protuberances, the more likely the birds are to be males. It is faulty reasoning as this size is more reflective of the bird's age. As the birds mature, a noticeable, shelf-like projection can sometimes be felt along the sides of the females above the thighs. This method of sexing does require that each bird be caught and individually examined.

Catching a guinea is no easy task, however. When my sister and I were quite small we lived in far north St. Louis County with a two-plus acre backyard enclosed in a six-foot-high cyclone fence. In it we had just about every feathered creature, including a small troop of guineas. On the last day of school each spring Dad would offer my sister and I a dollar for each of those guineas we could catch and bring to him. Thus he was assured a summer break free of too many interruptions from us, and it never cost him a dollar.

The key to catching an adult guinea, which I eventually did learn, was the same as is needed to play a good game of checkers. You have to be planning your moves well ahead of your feathered competition. And it doesn't hurt to have a wide-mouthed, long-handled net. I once saw an escaped guinea swept from the air at a farmers' market with such a net. I don't know who was the more surprised, the guinea or the net wielder. Guineas are truly flighty birds, and once netted they must be quickly brought to hand to prevent injury to themselves. And it is best that they be quite closely contained when cooped. For safest handling guineas should be carried by the wings, as their efforts to escape can cause injuries if the birds are carried by the legs. Clipping the flight feathers on one wing will prevent much flying activity; it renders the birds unbalanced and easier to contain. A common practice is to clip the feathers of the left wing. Reproductive organs are paired in most fowl, but generally it is only those on the left side that become fully developed and productive. Thus, the left side of a fowl is often slightly but measurably heavier.

As the birds mature the sexes do develop distinctive vocalizations or calls. The females will produce a distinct "buckwheat" call and the males a rapid-fire "keykeykey" call. For exact sexing you have to be standing close by when the birds begin to call so the individuals can be identified as to that call. They have to be well-grown birds, and permanent identification methods such as different colored leg bands can then be applied to the birds if needed. To hasten and facilitate sexing the birds, they can be caught from the roost and then cooped. A single bird is then removed from the cooped birds, placed in a coop of its own, and moved out of the line of sight but still within earshot of the others in the coops. They will soon begin calling to each other. By watching closely, you can soon pinpoint the males and females within the coop or coops. We strove to keep one male for every two to three hens and always kept a couple of extra or insurance males. We have had too many birds simply vanish during a day of ranging to feel comfortable relying on just a handful of breeding birds. Most of the farm flocks of my youth were of eight to twelve birds.

There are some measures that are helpful with transporting especially flighty birds that will work well with most all types of domestic fowl. Years ago I fell heir to an old cockfighter's traveling box. It resembled a black, metal-clad suitcase. The top half of one side opened on a piano hinge and was held closed with three snap latches. The unhinged side was actually a fine mesh wire that was painted black. The inside of the box was also painted black. The interior of the box was thus dark and calming, and the mesh side could be turned to the wall to prevent disturbances caused by passersby. It was meant to transport one battle stag but was large enough for a couple of large hens or guineas. I used it for several years to take a banty hen and chicks to school for show and tell. Some years ago I traded for a breeding trio of Blue Wyandottes from a fellow breeder in Ohio. Late one evening he placed the trio in a traveling box inside the covered bed of his pickup. The box had a solid bottom and sides, was painted black inside and out, and was topped with black painted wire mesh. He pulled into my poultry yard before daylight, and the hens laid their first day here and continued to lay well into the fall when their normal molt occurred.

While working on a SARE grant, I once did an experiment of housing various breeding groups of poultry in British-style field arks. The arks worked well with large-fowl chickens and ducks, but I agreed with a friend who said the real challenge would be to produce fertile eggs from a guinea trio so contained.

We positioned the ark in a less-traveled part of the poultry yard, watched them only from a distance, and for the first few days went only once a day to feed and water them as they settled into their new quarters.

Within a week they had made peace with their new home. I could lay my hands on the wire without a whir of wings and frantic behavior, and the hens soon began to lay in a darkened nest box in the rear corner of the ark. And, yes, those eggs were fertile. Containment that close was at odds with the reasons most folks own guinea fowl, but it did prove that the species could be placed into tightly managed environments where the matings could be carefully controlled.

We and many others have kept a small flock of guineas about the place for years on end with very little in the way of care beyond a bit of supplemental feed and shelter in the cold times. My friend Neal Gray of Alabama, in a drier and warmer climate than ours, has a flock of guineas that will naturally maintain their numbers from stolen out nests.

Guinea eggs are edible, though small, and they do follow a seasonable pattern of egg production, generally not starting to lay until mid to late spring. Egg production will vary from female to female and can range from forty to one hundred eggs per female per season. If left to nest on their own they will lay around twenty eggs before going broody. I have heard it said that all of the females bred to the same male will lay in a single nest, but I would not go to the bank with that one. Guinea eggs can replace chicken eggs one-to-one in many uses, although the yolk will make up a greater percentage of the egg. They aren't kept for their eggs, however. Rather they have been a sort of feathered novelty, earning their keep by announcing the intrusive arrival of hawks and feed salesmen and providing an occasional youngster to be fried.

They are more valued on the table by other cultures, but the arrival on the poultry scene of the growthier French or Jumbo guinea attests that there is some interest in the bird's meat, and a place in the market might grow. Here in the Midwest, for the moment, guineas are a farmer-to-farmer sale. Squab and even pheasant are at least something that most have heard of, but I suspect that more U.S. consumers have now eaten ostrich than guinea.

I don't expect to be passed on the highway by a tractor-trailer load of cooped guineas any time soon, but thirty years ago who had heard the term "range broiler"? There are pictures of guinea fowl on monuments in Egypt, and no one can deny that we have seen growing interest in a number of minor and exotic poultry species. There is a potential in them; many have a strong preference for dark poultry meat, and here is a bird that produces it in a most savory form. I haven't seen any "Guinea—The Other Dark Meat" bumper stickers, but with imaginative marketing who can say what can be done with this bird? I wouldn't try to build a farm based on a flock of guineas, but let Martha Stewart roast one for Thanksgiving and Rachel Ray make guinea burgers from the leftovers, and the guinea rush will be on!

It would not be realistic to believe that we will someday be consuming pigeons and guineas in place of broilers and turkeys, but it would certainly be nice to have some alternatives. Imaginative producers are taking them up in modest numbers to present such alternatives, to address the growing interest in food items with traditional roots, and to further broaden a position in the marketplace.

As I write this, a fusion of regional and local foods with international cuisines is emerging on the food scene. There is a restaurant in Tennessee that features Italian dishes made with Southern regional crops and meats. In such a scene the guinea could literally have its day.

A dark, stalking fear in the poultry renaissance has been the belief that it is too fad driven, that it smacks of what happened with "exotic animals" a decade or so back. The fast buck and faddishness have dogged production agriculture since at least the 1600s and the tulip craze that swept Europe. In America there was the Shorthorn craze of the nineteenth century and the fads like the pot-bellied pig that came along when the farm economy was foundering in the 1980s and 1990s. And some of this fervor has been seen with some poultry varieties, especially on the Internet.

A very real fear has emerged that the commercial poultry sector has come to rely far too much on a very small handful of poultry breeds and the hybrids derived from them. Some lines have had their genetic variability factors narrowed by a full 50 percent. Though bred in huge numbers, this makes them highly vulnerable to potentially deeply buried genetic ills (remember dwarfism in beef cattle?) and challenges from health and environmental issues for which they have no potential genetic response. The small numbers of birds outside of the family farm sector may be the only recourse in the event of such a challenge or breakdown.

Most raisers will keep just a handful of guineas—a trio up to a group of seldom more than ten or twelve—just to have them around the place like their parents or grandparents did. A few may be eaten and even some eggs gathered for the table, but they are most valued as feathered watchdogs and for their ability to keep pest insects in check. Those two roles still remain as significant selling points for guinea fowl. They are sold in small lots for these ends perhaps more than any other. The ability to supply them in lots of five to ten without shipping costs and complications adds value to them in local markets. Many will seek out this number to raise with a small lot of baby chicks to get a start of birds that are fixed to a home farm or smallholding.

The guinea, while not a feathered conundrum, does present something to ponder. Its future will be very much in the hands of those who take it up. There is now an association for guinea producers, and the bird has made its way into the showroom. However, lacking a KFG, those building a flock of guineas are going to have to make of them what they will in the marketplace. It may mean giving away a guinea fryer with every six broilers sold, taking guinea-based dishes to every church supper in the township, and becoming the answer man or woman for guineas on the local scene and in local markets. It could begin with something as simple as launching a flock with a color variety not seen in your area. A friend speaks of a flock of two hundred–plus guineas his mother once raised decades ago. They ranged across their farm's pastures eating insects and making much noise when a hawk passed over head. A flock of two hundred guineas would be very much a novel sight now, but an order for two hundred dressed guineas might be a closer economic reality than many of us assume.

Yes, they are very much something to ponder.

CHAPTER 6

Game Birds and Ornamentals

Quail, Peafowl, and Pheasants

BOBWHITE QUAIL

I f you were to throw the broadest poultry loop possible, it would settle down over two unique groups of fowl: game birds and ornamentals. The two groups are closely tied; the primary members of the ornamentals group are pheasants and pheasant-related birds such as the peafowl. They are the pretty birds of poultrydom, although many are also highly valued as table fowl. And they are not the easiest of God's winged creatures to keep and propagate. I have tried my hand at pheasant keeping with a trio of black-feathered birds and quickly found that they were just not the right fit for our small farm and my goals as a poultry producer. Many are quite flighty, have special and extensive penning needs, are seasonal as to reproduction (with a few exceptions), and can require special brooding measures. They are not inexpensive, have a reputation as hobbyist fowl, and those defined as game birds can have some special legal restrictions as to their keeping and propagation and sale.

Among the regulars at our community bird market is a bird dog trainer that grows out a good number of Bobwhite quail from hatchlings each year, a breeder of several varieties of peafowl, several producers with small groups of Coturnix quail, and an older producer with a few pair of ornamental pheasants. You will not see these birds at every market. Some cannot be sold without detailed paperwork, and they are not always easily transported. Though many might ooh and aah over their vivid colors and feathering, only a relative few are up to taking them home and making them work when they get there.

Inquiries about such birds are on the increase, and many of the larger shipping hatcheries now offer game birds and ornamentals in a fairly good variety. They are usually offered in rather small lots, often with a small group of guineas included to provide added security and warmth in shipment. The little guineas may also help them to get off to a better start in the brooder.

Upon glimpsing a male peafowl in full plumage, it's hard not to be impressed by the bird's beautiful colors and impressive size. Shortly after that, however, the cold hand of practicality reaches down from the mind to grip the heart, and the question that it squeezes out is, "What do you do with them?"

In times past they were eaten, and history records some very unusual dishes of blended fowl and meat cuts arriving at the table with a peafowl cape setting them off. I suspect that roast peafowl now would put off even the most ardent of the foodies. And you certainly won't see little cups of peafowl "nuggets" being offered at your local Walmart store any time soon.

The peafowl is a really, really big pheasant, one that takes time to reach full maturity, and some have been known to have a bit of an attitude. The peacock typically doesn't come fully into his own until his third year of life, and peahens should not be selected out until they reach the age of two. It is said that all things beautiful must have one great fault, and for the peafowl it is a voice that has been likened to a human scream. Its sound carries across great distances. We once had neighbors that lived about five miles away as the crow flies, or seemingly much closer as the peacock shrieks.

The males like a bit of purchase from which to survey their farmyard domain. They will fly up ten to fifteen feet or more and then swoop down at the oddest moments. The previously mentioned neighbors kept peafowl to adorn the grounds around their turkey hatchery. One spring morning one of their larger males flew down on their hired man, an older man of slight stature, and gave him quite a jar and some claw injuries. They do seem to love to fly up on any vehicles parked in their territory. I have heard it said that if you filled a forty-acre field with wrecked white Cadillacs and one new white Cadillac and then set a peacock loose, he would be atop the new car in less than five minutes.

Peafowl are bred in a great many colors and shadings including Blue Indie, Green-Shouldered, Black-Shouldered, Purple, White, Oaten, Pied, and more. The most common varieties are the Blue Indie, Black-Shouldered, and White. In our area you can expect to pay $150.00 to $250.00 for a yearling pair of better quality birds. In this part of the world peafowl fever always seems to cool somewhat in late summer and fall, and some bargains may be found for those willing to grow and winter birds before they feather up anew. At this time young peafowl can still be shipped via express mail, but the shipping costs, including the box, are apt to rival the costs of the young birds themselves.

Peachicks generally sell for between forty and sixty dollars each, depending on their color and rarity. They are most often sold in lots of eight hatchlings (as-hatched) with a few filler guinea keets required to keep them warm in transit. A few hatcheries will offer packages of four "assorted" peachicks and fifteen guinea keets for between $250.00 and $350.00. In this instance, as auctioneers will tell you at a fast-paced cattle auction, "Boys, you're taking 'em like you took your wife, for better or for worse."

Do not try to extrapolate what you know about tending turkeys to the care and rearing of peafowl. Yes, they are two of the largest of the more commonly kept poultry varieties, but they are very different birds—very different indeed. The turkey originated in the Americas. North America is its home turf, and it continues to flourish here in the wild. The peafowl originated in the very different, warmer region of Asia and maintains much more extensive and elaborate feathering. To put it in simple terms, it is a complex bird a long way from home.

The Show-Me State is currently home to two of the larger peafowl breeders in the United States who are, in point of fact, related. One keeps his breeding birds in elevated, wire-floored runs, and the other does not let his young birds to touch the ground for the whole of their first twelve months of life. The birds are vulnerable to parasite loads and damage, and a regular peacock course of worming under veterinary supervision is recommended. Our nearby producer worms his birds twice each year—spring and early fall—with the product Panacur. He uses it at the rate of three cubic centimeters per gallon of drinking water

A one-year-old peahen may lay an egg or two, but there will be some real questions as to their fertility if she has been running with a young male. The males will not fully feather until they are three years of age, and at two years of age it will be best to match the young male with no more than two like-aged females. He may, however, choose only to bond with one female at that age.

At three and beyond a male can accommodate up to four females. Some will even chance adding another peahen to that group, but dominant females may quickly emerge. Any more than four females and the low bird in the pecking order may not produce any fertile eggs. And four hens should produce quite adequate numbers for those producing strictly into local market outlets if given good care.

A peafowl egg takes twenty-eight days to hatch. A peahen will lay a clutch of four or so eggs and then go broody. If the eggs are regularly collected as they are laid, a peahen may continue to lay up to twenty eggs or a bit more. They are rather large eggs, and many consider them some of the most difficult to hatch by artificial means. Our farmers' market group has a shared cabinet incubator operated by a lady with a real knack for getting eggs of all kinds hatched. Peafowl eggs give her perhaps the greatest challenge, and she relates that a good year of hatching may be followed by a very poor one with eggs from the same flock and breeding program.

Younger birds especially seem to produce a great many clear eggs in their first breeding season.

Some years ago an older lady from a nearby county developed her own line of broody hens by combining large fowl Buff Orpington and Silkie fowl genetics. They were little egg-hatching machines and would even hunker down on golf balls if given a chance. Late each spring she would come to our market with several of these hens each brooding three or four peachicks, Indie Blues mostly, that they had hatched.

Invariably with peafowl, just about the time you think you're getting things figured out, along will come a new wrinkle or six. I have seen the birds kept at amusement parks to entertain the folks sitting in rest areas, used to draw attention to a business, added to bring something flashy and exotic to an aviary, and even used as animated lawn ornaments.

Each spring, as I visit bird markets around the area, I see male peafowl arrive with their massive tails flowing out of all sorts of imaginative crating that has been built to transport them. It is the time when they sell the best. They do draw the onlookers in great numbers; everyone seems to have a peacock story to tell. Generally a few tail feathers change hands for a dollar or two apiece (people carry them away like balloons on strings), and there are lots of wistful looks among those who gather around the coops. Still, a pair or trio, the best number for a starting point, represents an investment that many are reluctant to make in a bird for which even Martha Stewart lacks recipes.

Many find it easier to scratch the ornamental itch with one of the more commonly available fancy pheasants, such as the Red Golden, Yellow Golden, Lady Amherst's, Reeves's, Silver, or Dark-Throated Golden.

The Red Golden and Yellow Golden are even more vividly colored than most peafowl when in their breeding finery. The Silver, Lady Amherst's, and Reeves's also have extensive tail feathering in their own right. While all of these are bred for elaborate coloring and feathering, they do retain much of the more flighty nature and temperament of their wild cousins. They are far from a beginner's bird, and those who do well with them have done so through a true and often extended hands-on learning process.

As a youngster I enjoyed trips to the St. Louis Zoo. It is a zoo with an international reputation, but rather than the big cats and the elephants I was drawn to an older aviary setup in a far corner of the zoo grounds. It was a simple wooden structure, possibly one of the oldest on the grounds, but home to some of the rarest pheasants on earth. Their keeper was widely known for his expertise, and he kept and propagated birds from all over the world. Some were plain fowl whose feathering gave them needed camouflage in their native habitat. And even the most vividly colored lose their color as the breeding season passes and the molt arrives. The zoo's aviculturist was said to nearly live with those birds at times, he was a student of them at all times, and often created on the spot needed items of equipment and solutions to problems. It was there, over forty years ago, that I first saw seeds sprouted to produce year-around green feed for birds.

Pheasant chicks, like wild game bird hatchlings, are rather drab little creatures. In point of fact, adult birds may not achieve full color and feathering until they are two to three years of age. And the males are always more vividly colored and highly mannered than the females.

The incubation period for pheasant eggs is twenty-three to twenty-five days, and most producers keep these birds in breeding pairs. We had a friend that kept several pairs of Red Goldens, and he would occasionally keep a breeding trio, but they had to be carefully selected and were more closely monitored when in the breeding pen. He believed the Red Goldens to be the easiest to handle and propagate. He kept the greatest number of Red Goldens, along with a few pairs of Yellow Goldens. Typically, he would produce 50 to 125 pheasant chicks each year, selling about half as chicks and the remainder as sexed pairs of adolescent and breeding age birds. Surplus males he would hold to sell when in full feather, and he would get up to fifty dollars each for such birds. This was when the novelty factor really kicked into high gear in the market, and with their vivid red coloring they do catch the eye. And I do suppose they could even make some rather pricey pheasant on toast points. They are also the variety that seems to perform the best in simple housing here in northeast Missouri.

Our friend built his pheasant pens along the south-facing sidewall of a large farm building. They were roughly eight feet deep by ten feet wide by six feet high. They were earthen floored, and into one corner of each (covering about a third of the pen floor area) he created an open pile of pine and cedar limbs.

Those piles provided cover and comfort zones for the birds. They would shelter and dust beneath them, and the piles gave the birds something to fly up on and sun themselves. Their primary shelter was provided by a fifty-five-gallon plastic drum sawed into two parts lengthwise. It was formed by cutting away roughly one-third of the barrel. A simple pop hole of about eight inches by eight inches was cut into the larger barrel segment at the center point. It was then placed at the back of the pen, against the building wall, and a bit of earth was packed around it to hold it in place.

The pens had solid tops to protect from the sun and prevent the rain from causing mud problems. It also prevented the birds from being stressed by wild birds flying overhead. In cold and wet weather the pen fronts and ends would be sheathed with plastic or inexpensive tarping. You have to be careful to not enclose poultry too tightly in inclement weather as it can lead to problems with air exchange and quality. If you can smell ammonia in the birds' quarters they are probably being contained too tightly, and respiratory problems could soon follow. Access was through a walk-in door in the front of each pen. The birds were at some distance from the areas of the farmyard with greatest foot traffic, strangers were absolutely kept away from them, and he would approach the pens while whistling or softly talking to the birds to avoid giving them a start.

He would hatch pheasant eggs in the small cabinet incubators that he used for the chickens he also raised. To rear them in box brooders he used red attractor lights, or, with heat bulbs, he would use the infrared variety. The brooding room was kept darkened, and he avoided sudden shifts of light patterns around the young birds. I have seen brooder rooms where even the overhead lights contained red-hued bulbs.

A real boon to the keepers of ornamentals and game birds in recent years has been the development and greater availability of a wide variety of game bird feeds. Many feed companies now offer full game bird feed lines including starters, grower feeds, breeders' rations, and conditioning or maintenance feed formulations. They are generally sold in a small crumble form, and they aren't cheap. The birds, even the adults, consume very small amounts of feed daily. To assure good health and development such feeds have to be very nutrient dense and of appropriate particle size for the age and species of the bird.

One quail producer of my acquaintance got into a bit of trouble with his good wife for slipping her kitchen blender out of the house to further crush starter feed for some of his little quail. He was quickly sent to the local secondhand store to buy a blender of his own and joined the ranks of producers who regularly reduce feed particle size for some of their smaller varieties.

Some have used turkey feeds in a pinch, but to be a good steward of these birds you cannot shortchange them on their feedstuffs. Good care mandates quality feedstuffs with a consistent formulation. These are expensive birds, sometimes quite difficult to acquire, and are an investment where you cannot cut corners to save a few pennies just on the feed bill.

Ornamental pheasant chicks generally run $12 to $20 each, and a few hatcheries do offer them in lots of twenty-five chicks containing two or three different varieties (and generally it is the supplier's choice as to the breeds that go into the box). A pair of adolescents will generally bring $85 to $125, and express mail will double that cost to get them onto the farm or smallholding. I have seen some mature pairs offered at bird swaps over the years, but they are often an instance for the buyer to beware. They can be older birds, birds that have proven to be very flighty, or birds with poor reproductive performance. I have seen veteran producers of most poultry species wrest at least some performance out of bad stock, but it is never good to try to make a beginning with someone else's problems. Do your homework, ask lots of questions, and don't be taken in by all of the pretty colors. And a lesson that more than one greenhorn has learned the hard way is that two old males in a molted out state are still considered a pair. Two of anything is always a "pair" of sorts.

I cannot emphasize enough that an early and large investment needs to be made in garnering knowledge of ornamentals and game birds before investing in them on the hoof. A number of detailed books on pheasant, quail, and peafowl care are available. Visits with veteran breeders should be scheduled and dependable sources of feedstuffs and health products lined up before acquiring even the first bird. I have known of birds being taken back by the seller after some rather large checks have changed hands because the buyer has asked, "All right, what do I feed them?"

Peafowl and ornamental pheasants are birds most of us are going to have to scramble to have a reason to buy. A peafowl producer of some renown here in Missouri has recently had yearly sales of around three hundred birds and calls them the most successful of his decades in peafowl rearing. He maintains a great many birds of different ages as his best sellers are males in full plumage with a hen or two to go along with them. Thus he has crops of breeding birds, youngsters, yearlings, two year olds, and three year olds on his farm. That is a lot of game bird feed to buy on a weekly basis and a lot of birds to tend.

Anything beyond a hobby with these birds will depend on positioning yourself as the "pheasant guy" or the "peafowl lady" for your area.

Through your birds you should also be marketing your acquired expertise. This means that there will be much in the way of follow-up after each sale, but the producer can and should position himself in this, also. It can be with further sales of stock, supplying needed feed or equipment, or even charging something in the way of a consultation fee. You aren't going to find a lot of veterinarians who will know what to do for a pheasant with a "raspy" throat. Marketing your birds will greatly depend on getting you and your birds to the people most likely to value and want them. The boys at the coffee shop and down at the coop aren't going to buy a lot of Silver Pheasants.

After obtaining green-headed ducks for their lakes, rurban types tend to want a peacock or two to strut about the yard. It is a sort of rural Gatsby thing, I guess, but they are living and breathing creatures that will need a lot more care than a whole gross of plastic pink flamingos. It just may be that further income could accrue to those who could consult on their care, provide feedstuffs, and provide services such as custom hatching. Keep in mind that a lot of these sorts of birds are given back after folks have had a month or two for that whole pretty bird thing to wear off.

With these birds, like real estate, location is going to be an important factor. I have to honestly question just how many peafowl you are going to sell off of a mountainside holding in northern Montana. Our friend with peafowl has essentially created a peafowl store serving much of the Midwest. His family's birds have been featured in many regional magazine articles and newspaper stories, and he travels to many poultry events and markets across several states.

I field a lot of calls from people with an older pair of peafowl or a single bird (the mate has died) for sale after owning them for a time. As Dad liked to say, the shine had worn off, and they weren't wanting to put in the needed effort to keep them going. These callers do, however, all too often expect to get all of their money back and then some. That ain't gonna happen. It's hard to get any kind of large bird sold, especially going into winter.

Game bird production has emerged as a steadily growing venture for many, but one with aspects not common to other types of poultry ventures. A number of game birds are started and reared in our area for training hunting dogs and stocking shooting preserves. And I received a recent call from a broker seeking one thousand quail for the restaurant trade in the St. Louis area.

Game birds generally refer to Ring-necked pheasants, their derivatives, and the various quail varieties that can be found in the wild. Game fowl in North America also include Canada geese, other wild goose varieties, the numerous varieties of wild duck, and a great many strains of wild turkey. They are the birds of the field that can be brought under the gun during legal hunting seasons. And they are all vigorously protected by different state and federal conservation laws. Under an interpretation of Missouri law, game birds are any that occur naturally within the borders of the state, even if just as a part of their migration pattern. There are special laws for migratory birds, waterfowl in this instance, that involve both state and federal authorities. You do not simply pluck a few of these birds out of the wild and go about propagating them. As a matter of fact, you can get put away for a fair bit of time just for trying that sort of thing. Few are the springs when I am not asked about hatching the eggs from a quail or turkey nest that someone has uncovered. My answer is a flat no and to advise the local conservation officer if such a nest is detected.

Each state will set its own rules as to how game birds are to be kept and propagated in private hands within its borders. These regulations should be available from the local conservation agent or game warden and are included in each state's wildlife codes. Keeping such birds will generally require some sort of licensing and may subject the producer to on-site inspections of his or her facilities to ascertain that the birds are not being kept in an overcrowded, unhealthy, or inhumane manner. There may also be multiple levels of licensing covering hobbyists, dog trainers, breeders, and shooting preserves. Documents of transference may be required for the birds under such laws, and live birds allowed transfer only between duly licensed buyers and sellers.

Investigate those laws fully and make sure that everything about keeping game birds is fully understood. A federal permit will often be required for keeping migratory fowl such as the Canada goose.

As of this writing Missouri has two levels of licensing that I feel are somewhat typical of the licensing requirements you will find across the country. There is a hobbyists' license that limits ownership to fifty or fewer game birds of the state in a year. These are birds indigenous to the state but not taken from the wild. A second, higher priced license is for game bird breeders, has no numbers limit, and allows the regulated sale of any birds produced.

Get everything right before getting started with game birds, and work with the conservation authority in your area rather than viewing it as something adversarial. Some of the earliest writing I ever did was for the magazine of the Missouri Department of Conservation, the *Missouri Conservationist*. I was a farm boy, grew up hunting and fishing, and early on I learned that there was much to be gained by working with our state conservation agency to develop the resources of the family farm. They helped us with tree plantings and timber harvest, development of a fee fishing venture, and establishing plantings for wildlife.

Wildlife code laws are some of the easiest to violate. Like the rules of golf, they call for the participants of the pursuit to be ethical ladies and gentlemen. It is the way most farm folk play the game of life, too, and the integrity and continuation of this form of production hinges on producers being respectful and observant of all the laws and regulations that apply to them.

With game birds you definitely must have complex facilities in place, and this may even be a condition for receiving licensing. Licensing agencies may reserve the right to conduct unannounced inspections of such facilities at any time. They do so out of a concern for the birds that should be shared by the producer and that will be appreciated and valued by the consumer.

Game birds are high-strung creatures. Producers that I have known report best results working with more tractable birds such as Chukar partridge and some of the quail varieties. Pheasants are larger, hard-flying birds, and they have value to hunting preserves only if those traits are cultivated in the birds.

Building a system of flight pens to house breeding and developing birds can be quite expensive. The pens must be topped, of good height to allow for safe flight, and they must provide protection from predators at ground level and below. I have seen flight cages for a few birds made as simply as unrolling pliable fence-topping mesh over a couple of low-growing trees and weighing and staking it down around a modest perimeter. The portal into it is often little more than an overlapping of the mesh ends that are pinned shut. I can't recommend this particular system, but it does show the importance of imagination and creativity to incorporate a venture such as this into a small farm enterprise mix. Where snow loads can be a problem, flight cages must be rigidly reinforced. A lot of birds are lost simply through blow down and other weather damage to flight pens. It may be necessary to go out after a big storm and push or rake any snow off of the pens before the accumulation becomes too great.

Quite honestly, the best advice I can give about building flight and breeding enclosures is to seek out the input of conservation agents and established producers in your immediate area. Factors such as soil type and annual rainfall will bear heavily on the design and construction of these larger pens. There is also strong evidence that the mineral content of the soil will impact on reproduction and egg quality.

We live in an area of northeastern Missouri where wild stocking of Ring-necked pheasants was attempted several decades ago. The stocking did not take, as the soil type and other factors were not conducive to sustaining viable breeding populations. An occasional bird will still fly up, perhaps an escaped bird or one released by a hobbyist, but there is a belief that a few "wild" birds still remain in the region. And it is interesting to note that the county just southwest of us does support a small but viable population of Prairie Chickens.

There can be some problems with the definitions some states have set down as to just what is and isn't a game bird. Here in Missouri the Tennessee Red quail does not occur in the wild, but the Bobwhite does. When mated together they will produce young resembling the Bobwhite. I have heard of some field agents terming them as birds of wild origin and some saying no.

The Muscovy duck, the duck of the New World, not descended from the Mallard, has caused a similar stir of late. They are a wild duck in parts of South America, but are not wide ranging and have been kept as a domestic duck in the United States for decades. A feral population of them was recently detected in three Texas counties along the Mexican border. This discovery has somewhat clouded the status of the Muscovy duck in the United States. Some believe that this population is derived from escaped and abandoned ducks, but others believe that it just might be a naturally occurring population. A fair number of waterfowl get swept into the wild each year by flooding, and an awful lot of Easter and other ducks get dumped into parks and along waterways each year. As it was being sorted out, Muscovy ducks were almost termed migratory fowl, and the controversy has not yet been put fully to rest.

With Ring-necked pheasants the males have far greater value than the females. Major suppliers of pheasant chicks will often sell hen chicks for as little as twenty to twenty-five cents each if bought in lots of several hundred. Ring-necked pheasants are sold in several varietals including melanistic mutants, a white varietal, hybrids bred for extra size or speed on the wing, and in many hues. For legal matters and to be on the safe side I would assume all to be called Ring-necks and subject to licensing for their possession and propagation.

I have a good friend whose family has been involved in pheasant rearing for three generations. They developed a line of substantial size and calm nature. He had one male that would actually ride on his shoulder as he went about doing chores. A calmer strain would be of great value to those producing Ring-necked pheasants for sale as meat birds. They would be at odds with those supplying birds to shooting preserves and for dog training but would have greater survival rates and be far easier to handle for those supplying the table trade.

A number of quail varieties call the United States home, including the Bobwhite, Blue Scale, California Valley, and Gambrel. Other than the Bobwhite they tend to occupy rather fine niches in the natural environment, though in huntable numbers in some of those areas. The Bobwhite is by far the most common and has the widest range. It is the bird most envision when and if they chance to think about quail.

If the variety is not native to your region it can probably be held without licensing, but invest in a phone call to your local conservation authority just to be sure. The Bobwhite is the bird that most associate with quail on the table and there have been strains developed with mature weights a fair bit larger than birds of wild stock. A couple of ounces is a big jump up in quail weight, and a brace, two birds, is often considered the traditional serving portion for quail.

Quail and pheasant chicks are high-strung from the egg on, and this, coupled with their smaller size, can make them a bit of a challenge to get brooded successfully. As noted earlier, it was once a fairly common practice to hatch and brood pheasant chicks under large fowl Game chickens. Artificial brooding is best accomplished in a darkened room under red brooder lights. Even some quail chicks can have a nervous and even an aggressive nature with each other. The producer must be on constant watch for early signs of feather picking and cannibalism. The varieties should be raised separately. Human traffic should be kept to a minimum around them and loud noises and sudden shifts in light patterns avoided. Quail and pheasant chicks are generally shipped in lots of thirty to one hundred and will sell for between three and six dollars each in these smaller lots.

Due to the smaller size of the chicks, special feeding and watering equipment will be needed, including drown-proof waterer bases. And while some have used turkey feeds in a pinch, these little birds consume feed in such small amounts that it is crucial that it be of the best quality. As noted earlier, some even take the step of processing starter feeds into even smaller particles to make sure the little birds get good levels of consumption. Here it is best to just swallow hard and buy into a feeding program put together strictly for game birds. Such programs are now available from most of the major feed companies, many of which keep nutritionists on staff that can help with some questions about game bird care and management.

Upon arrival all hatchlings will benefit from being placed directly into well-prepared and warmed brooder units. Brooder heating should be turned on at least twenty-four hours before the hatchlings arrive, the units should be free of accumulated dust, and the heating elements should be working well, with fresh bulbs and backups in place. The first drinking water offered should be a bit warm and perhaps fortified with a spoonful or so of sugar per pint. A good vitamin/electrolyte product could also be offered in the drinking water for the first three or four days and then once or twice a week thereafter until the hatchlings are about eight weeks old. It is a good product to have on hand for any time the birds have encountered some sort of stress. These are far from bomb-proof birds despite their hardy nature suited to life in the wild. They can be flighty little box bombs, and some may even injure or kill themselves by flying into top netting or other containment structures.

There are selling opportunities for game birds, but they are not something akin to chicken broilers or holiday turkeys that "everyone" is open to buying and preparing in familiar manners of cooking. What I have encountered is that they can be sold from the farm in fair numbers to some rather specific niche markets.

Restaurants, for example, are going to need a steady supply of game birds if they are to make them a standard menu item. Even though game meats are gaining in popularity, there is a seasonal pattern as to how they are featured and consumed in the United States. Typically the fall and winter seasons see the greatest demand, and these are the seasons when consumers seem to prefer richer and more savory fare. Shooting preserves tend to have longer gunning seasons than those established by the various state conservation agencies for the harvesting of wild stocks of birds. A local preserve offers game bird hunting beginning about a month earlier than the state opening day and continues their season into the early spring. They are offering a hunting experience in times of more favorable weather and travel. A preserve may have the facilities to hold a certain number of birds on site, but it will need a dependable supply throughout its operating year, maybe even the year around if dogs are being trained there. They will require healthy birds that are in good plumage and color and that are strong flyers. And, with pheasants, there is clearly a strong preference for male birds. Quail that have evolved for a specific region cannot be sowed willy-nilly across the landscape. People who want to hunt Bobwhite or Gambel's or other quail want to shoot them where they are the wild norm.

Costs to acquire good seedstock and the time commitment, including the time for marketing and the special handling they may require, must be weighed heavily in the decision to produce game birds. I have tinkered a bit with pheasants. I certainly like them on the plate, and I can see some real potential in marketing them as a fancy table bird, but it is going to be a costly trek that will be uphill all the way. Overnight half a brood or more of young quail or pheasants can be lost, and with these birds just about all of your learning will have to be done by doing. The veteran producers each seem to have their own systems of operation developed after years of trial and error; they have found the sources of stock upon which they can rely and build, and they have made the commitment to be "the man" or "the woman" for such birds in their area.

There are kindred birds that can be raised that are somewhat easier to tend and may even be a bit more forgiving in their care needs. The Painted quail and Button quail are colorful little ornamentals that many keep in aviaries in which the environment is carefully regulated. A nearby nursing facility, for a time, kept a four-foot-by-four-foot-by-eight-foot indoor aviary for the enjoyment of their residents. It was a pleasure to view, but took an hour or two of time each day for the housekeeping staff to service and maintain. There were also periodic calls by the folks that supplied and stocked it (they had a small business providing these units to different firms needing such displays). The aviary included finches and other small, sociable cage birds along with a couple of pairs of Button quail that lived at floor level. The quail cleaned up spilt bird seed and even produced a great many distinctive eggs that they did not incubate. They had to have the protection of a fully contained aviary, and their small size is such that they cannot cope with cold temperatures and harsh weather.

The bird that will fit into the greatest number of places and roles is the Japanese Coturnix of Pharaoh quail. They just may be the ideal backyard, basement, garage, or corner-of-the-barnloft bird. They are small, quiet, of good temperament, easy to handle, cost relatively little to feed, and they are quail. They are not quail like the Bobwhite; in fact many bird dog trainers will not use them to train dogs for field work on wild birds. And, yes, they are fairly small birds with mature weights in the eight-to-ten-ounce range. The Standard or Brown Coturnix is the most commonly seen. It will have a mature weight to ten ounces or even a bit more and will lay like the dickens, beginning to produce eggs at a very few weeks of age. Just as Missouri opossums are said to be born pregnant, these little gals are almost hatched a-laying.

A pen as small as one foot by one foot by three feet will hold two breeding trios of Coturnix quail. A number of companies over the years have developed stacking cage systems that make it possible to maintain substantial numbers of these birds and manage their wastes in a fairly small space.

They are rather vigorous little birds, but most in our area raise them in all-wire containment inside a building. It may be cold housing, but there is protection from direct sunlight, drafts, and dampness. Quail-specific feeding and watering equipment should be used and the hatchlings brooded and managed like other game birds.

The Coturnix quail are bred in a number of colors, including blonde and white varietals. The more colorful varieties tend to have the lighter mature weights, but Texas A&M developed and lent its name to a white varietal that can have a mature weight of twelve to fourteen ounces. It was developed for quail meat production.

The Coturnix are voluminous egg producers, and their eggs are vividly spotted. They don't go broody, and the eggs must be artificially incubated. To give an idea of the size of these diminutive eggs, the chicken egg tray for a table-top Styrofoam incubator will hold forty-two eggs. The quail egg tray for such a unit will hold 108 eggs. These eggs have an eighteen-day incubation, and, due to the small size of the hatchlings, seedstock is generally offered only in the form of hatching eggs. A dozen such eggs will cost around two dollars per egg, and they seem to fare much better in shipment than most other hatching eggs. With a bit of time and study most producers become fairly good at sexing the little birds based on their coloring.

The Coturnix is a non-native variety anywhere in the United States, and I see them often at midwestern bird swaps. They are certainly a good beginner's bird, and many are adding a Coturnix venture of modest size to their poultry yard business. The little birds dress rather nicely and reproduce in the numbers and timely fashion to make them dependable meat birds. They are quite easy to handle and transport, and the brown strain of birds generally sell for two to three dollars each at local markets. The small size of the hatchlings and the higher costs for game bird feeds are what deter many from producing these birds. They must have dedicated brooders and grow out pens, and their prolific egg laying requires the producer to be ever busy at the marketing task.

The great number of eggs that the little hens produce has led many to develop imaginative ways to deal with that particular surplus. In artsy methods of food preparation and presentation, halved, hard-boiled quail eggs are now being used for both taste and visual enhancement of a number of dishes. The diminutive eggs hard boil to resemble hen eggs and catch the eye while lending themselves to recent trends of smaller serving sizes and more exotic foods and presentations. In the Midwest and elsewhere, pickled, hard-boiled eggs are classic bar food, along with pickled just about everything from pigs' feet to turkey gizzards. The pickled quail egg is a bite-sized version of this, and they do sell well when offered at local farmers' markets. A pint jar of them may bring eight to ten dollars or more, and consumers eagerly seek them out when available.

Members of our local marketing group, foodies themselves, went into Coturnix quail after a long period of of consideration. They were brown-egg and table-duck folks and thought the birds a good fit for their particular farm venture mix. The sales of meat birds did not pan out exactly as hoped. Processing such small birds can be time consuming, and there are far more people who have never eaten quail than have.

And, sadly, many have bad associations about any sort of game based on experiences with wild birds or animals that were poorly handled in the field or went long hours before seeing any sort of processing and proper storage. A quail full of shot, carried all day in a hunting coat and not dressed until after a long drive home, is going to be gamey—very gamey.

Quail and pheasant are an elite sort of poultry to keep. They are certainly challenging to rear, and for most people in this chicken-nugget era of ours they are more the stuff of myth and legend than actual fare for the family table. Unlike my grandfather, I didn't grow up having to hunt to eat, but game was no rarity on our table, and there were many Sunday dinners with quail and pheasant that followed Sunday morning hunters' breakfasts of squirrel and frog legs. These birds are now presenting an alternative to all who want something lean and different from the chicken and turkey that now dominate the marketplace and the table.

I have already advanced my theory that many are turned off such birds by early experiences with birds that were taken afield and then badly handled and processed. I worked for a few years at a Missouri Deer Check Station, and it's a wonder that people weren't literally dying from eating venison that was so poorly handled and transported.

For some it may not be politically correct to eat a brace of farm-raised, carefully tended, and thoughtfully processed quail that were pen raised. These folks are missing one of life's real eating pleasures, but to each his own. These birds are going to have a future in the market, and they will grow in importance as a venture to diversify to some farms and small holdings. They are being offered by more and more shipping hatcheries, and there are also a growing number of hatcheries and supply houses dedicated to just this category of fowl. Early efforts are under way to breed strains that grow faster and more efficiently. Some selective breeding for a calmer nature would be warranted in those larger strains being developed for the meat trade, too.

You no longer hear remarks about pheasant under glass symbolizing the good life like you did when I was a boy, but much consumer education is now needed as to just how quail and pheasant can and should be used. There are early stirrings that game meat is health food, even for those not on a paleo diet. A Kentucky Fried Peacock and Quail is not likely to pop up near you any time soon, and the task of getting the word out about these birds is going to fall squarely on the producer.

I have heard tales of an entrée served during the holidays in the New Orleans area: a turkey stuffed with duck stuffed with chicken stuffed with quail. If that catches on, all of us in the feather business will get rich. There is a seed for marketing here, however. The people buying turkeys, ducks, or chickens from you are all potential buyers of quail and pheasants. They just don't know it yet. Give them a bird or two to try, prepare handouts with recipes and a bit of background material, cover such birds in your newsletter, use the vividly colored birds on letterheads and business cards, and use the word "wings" in farm names and logos. Build on the positive elements in the images these birds have.

They're not for everyone, but they and their ornamental cousins can be niche players that bring in a fair number of those green pictures of dead presidents. Some years ago a family began working with a number of varieties of pheasants, quail, and other game birds and ornamentals. They document some of their experiences, good and bad, in articles submitted to the various small publications in the poultry field. Those articles are published, the farm grew in recognition, and their sales followed.

There is growing interest in these birds and the real need is not just for the birds, but for the producers of those birds who can and will share their knowledge of their care and uses.

Fowl Breeds

Nene Goose

Crested Bobwhite Quail

Peafowl

Wikimedia Commons

Chinese Geese

Ralph Daily/Wikimedia Commons

Emden Goose

Wikimedia Commons

Chinese Geese

Thinkstock

Fantail Pigeon

Broadbreasted White Turkey

Red Junglefowl

Guineas

Royale Photography/Wikimedia Commons

Ameraucana Cock

Pete Cooper/ Wikimedia Commons

Buff Orpington Chicken

Wikimedia Commons

Silver Sebright Hen

Thinkstock

Silkie Chicken

Thinkstock

The eggs of quail, ostrich, chicken (white-shelled and brown-shelled), and emu.

Pilgrim Geese

King Pigeons

African Goose

Indian Runner

Jim Gifford/Wikimedia Commons

Modena Pigeon

Wikimedia Commons

Homer Pigeon

Wikimedia Commons

Rakovnik Roller Red Pigeon

Jim Gifford/Wikimedia Commons

Turbit Pigeon

Dick Daniels/Wikimedia Commons

Bobwhite Quail

Luis Miguel Bugallo Sánchez/Wikimedia Commons

Coturnix Quail

Silver Ameraucana Pullet

Ring-necked Pheasant

Brenda Zaun/Wikimedia Commons

Nene Goose

Nevit Dilmen/Wikimedia Commons

Peafowl

Tamal Kanti Panja/Wikimedia Commons

Golden Pheasant

CHAPTER 7

Restoration and Marketing

Reaching and Educating Consumers

BUFF ORPINGTON

Before us now are opportunities in poultry keeping and production that, frankly, I thought would never be seen again in my lifetime. They aren't falling from the sky like big fluffy snowflakes, but they are being found by those with the creativity and initiative to make more of them than a momentary interest in the new or faddish.

American agriculture is diffusing into many different directions, including a new/old group of true family farmers and smallholders building on local food and farming traditions yet finding new outlets for their production. Many of them are now focusing beyond the recent boom in interest in brown eggs and range broilers and are seeking new courses beyond these already possibly maturing pursuits.

Americans are not going to stop consuming such historically important staples of their diet as the egg, chicken, and turkey. Ask the emu and ostrich people, the few that are left, if there were any cracks to be found in that trinity. However, looking beyond that troika and by working with and around its edges, many producers are coming to believe that alternative poultry species and systems of production will lead to a future that those with ostriches and emu did not find.

There is a very real need now for a better marketing infrastructure to aid in the advancement of all poultry, from heirloom broilers to guinea fowl. At this moment I am aware of just one publication providing anything in the way of detailed market reporting, and this only for a handful of poultry auctions in southeast Pennsylvania.

Our farming community is about seventy miles from the city of St. Louis, where there are upscale restaurants, specialty food stores, consumers with substantial disposable incomes, community groups involved with food issues, and many others that want and would pay well for the distinct and heirloom poultry varieties that the farmers in our area produce and can do so even in greater numbers. That distance, just over an hour's driving time, is as broad as any ocean, however. Missouri now has only two small abattoirs that will process poultry, there is no marketing apparatus to take poultry from the state's farms to all of those forks in the Show-Me State's urban areas, there are huge cultural and societal gaps to be spanned, government regulations thwart rather than smooth the path from family farm and consumer, and, honestly, we as farmers need to do a better job of standing up for ourselves and getting our own story told.

The other day a member of our farmers' market group was spending a leisurely Sunday afternoon puttering among the flowers in her yard. A car stopped at their roadside sign, a window rolled down, and, in uncertain English, a young woman asked if they had any eggs for sale. They did have eggs for sale and would have much more to sell as the year unfolded. The people in the car were Russian immigrants, the young woman the only one who spoke English, and they were many miles from their home looking for the farm-fresh items that they knew and valued from their earlier life. This was a bit of serendipity for both, but it also shows the information breakdown that occurs.

Our market members live in a community that is largely Amish, possibly the closest Amish community to the St. Louis area. The immigrants had, no doubt, heard that the Amish farmers often produced the farm goods that they sought. They did not know that the Amish would not open their gates and do business on Sunday. Thus a weedy flower bed created a marketing opportunity that might otherwise have been lost.

Our friends' family took the visitors on a tour of their small farm to show them the poultry yard, baby chicks and eggs in the incubator, newborn lambs, dairy goats, and the early work being done in the market garden. Those folks bought several dozen brown eggs—at St. Louis prices—and promised they would return when the young ducks and lambs were ready for harvest. A bit of good fortune and some simple country kindness spanned a very big gap for those two families, but it needs to be done much more often and on a much larger scale.

As land-grant college extension work continues its slide from relevance, many producers believe it is missing its real chance for a sustainable future by not stepping up to do more work linking farmers and consumers in the marketing process. There are farmers' markets near large urban areas, such as Miami and Chicago, where there is a growing presence for live birds and small stock. There are barriers of distance and culture that have to be crossed and be crossed while packing a fair-sized load of poultry yard denizens that quack, cackle, coo, and gobble.

In some camps I am accused of being too concerned about the "business" of poultry. For a number of years I was active in breeding, promoting, and reporting on the efforts to preserve a wide array of rare and endangered poultry breeds and varieties. Some breeds and varieties were indeed pulled back from the brink of extinction, and it became almost fashionable to have a few "heirloom" birds about the homeplace or backyard. Mostly hens, as all of those roosters were just too noisy. How spinsterhood preserved a breed was never made clear, however. Some thought that was enough, the job was done, and even got a bit smug about it. A few others, with some of the rarest and most minor of breeds, copped an attitude that they were going to take them to the grave with them.

I'm sorry, but preservation is but the first of a great many steps, and the real goal should be restoration. That means returning a breed or variety to the numbers, the number of producers, and the role for which it was developed at the time when it most prospered. And yes, that calls for a rethinking and a restructuring of virtually the whole of the production agriculture process. Nearly every poultry breed and variety was developed for practical ends, to work in specific environments and economic circumstances.

Eye appeal did come into play. After all, they were developed by human beings, and eye appeal and personal satisfaction are important factors to what makes a successful poultry venture and poultry producer. Still, preservation work cannot be considered fully successful until the various breeds and varieties are restored to the point where they are in a position to "pay their own way."

Poultry, like so many other livestock species, were first bred and kept to meet a family's needs and then to serve locally arising markets. And, yes, ducks, chickens, geese, turkeys, guineas, and more are livestock. They are cultivated for practical ends, historically have had an important economic role to play in the success of the family farm, and those practical ends are what continue to give them their greatest meaning and value.

Many of the varieties outlined here never had great commercial roles to play, but they will not thrive or even survive if left as mere novelties and lesser members of an avian sideshow. Not many people are going to dine on Carneau squab or young Pearl guinea any time soon, but if we are not continuing to breed them toward such practical ends, are we not really neglecting them in just one more way?

The handful of pigeons I added not long ago may never grow into a business as many think of production agriculture now. However, they are a bit more than just a feel-good purchase for me. I have been fielding a growing number of inquiries about squabbing pigeons, and a start has to be made to determine their worth as a venture in our area.

Most poultry ventures now being launched on a more human and artisanal scale are not about amassing and shuffling great amounts of money but serving a market concerned about the food items it is receiving and then allowing the producer to retain as much of the money generated as is possible.

When I was coming out of high school in the late 1960s and taking up a larger role in the family farm, a school of thought was emerging about how U.S. farm life would evolve. The belief was that there would come to pass a number of quite large operations producing certain crops and livestock as factory-farmed commodities. Alongside them would be a number of mid-sized, family farms providing some inputs to those larger farms and producing other crops and livestock that did not lend themselves to factory farming methods.

That had a short season to say the least. As the big farms grew ever larger and fewer in number they did so at the expense of those mid-sized farmers that were quickly bypassed by the technology and infrastructure that had become so enthralled with the ideas of mega-farms and farming.

The two livestock species first gobbled up by the factory farm sector were the chicken and the turkey. With these birds shut tightly away in sheet metal gulags, a sea of medium and large white eggs and broiler and turkey meat to be restructured and reshaped began to roll out. The good stewing hen, roasting goose, Long Island duckling, and pan-fried quail went the way of roasted buffalo haunch and Passenger pigeon on the menu. They were remembered by the old-timers, had often become little more than speech idioms, and were brought out at a few family reunions and special events, but they were no longer as accessible as they once were.

In the waning years of the twentieth century, consumers grew more concerned about how and what they were being fed. Awareness dawned that there had once been something better, that regional foods were once more rich and varied than what could be done with corn syrup, soy, and hothouse turkey. The range broiler and the cage-free brown egg grew out of a demand that agriculture again become something better and more reflective of society and issued a challenge to the agribusiness status quo. It was the opening for poultry folks to get back into the game. Basic food consumption patterns are always going to be price driven, a society will always be measured economically by the beans/chicken/beef yardstick, but societies and economies around the world are turning a corner. With increases in education and disposable income, consumers have learned that they can vote with their dollars. For a growing number of the population, food is becoming more than the cheapest amount of calories that can be bought to sustain life.

What was first done with wine is now being done with all sorts of farm products. When I graduated from high school the idea of a fine Missouri wine was all but laughable. Wine was made here, but on a par with bathtub gin and white corn likker. We had brown eggs when I was a youngster, too. They weren't store bought but came from small home flocks, from folks who were too cantankerous or too lacking in funds to go with the flow of agribusiness. Their brown-egg layers were homegrown and kept sustainably long before that word was to become fashionable. I remember Dad, upon witnessing the early stages of the environmental movement, saying that long ago his family had practiced recycling, but back then it was just another part of being poor.

Now there is nothing inherently better in a brown-shelled egg than in a white one. In fact, everything that adds value to a brown-shelled egg can be done with a white-shelled one. That includes organic production and coming from breeds with the bonafides to be termed heirloom. Modern consumers, as their circumstances progress, bring new and different demands into the marketplace. They want food production that they believe is more healthful, food that is more humanely produced and in a more environmentally sound manner, and that sustains the smaller, family farm–based agriculture with which they are most comfortable and trust the most. Somehow the brown egg became one of the icons of all of this, and in the growing demand for it and what it represents the way was opened for this modern poultry-keeping renaissance of ours. Because of its early rarity and association with small-flock production, the brown-shelled egg was valued quite highly and generated the sort of prices that have inspired so many to take a new look at poultry production in a more artisanal and less industrialized manner.

Recent economic events have caused brown egg and range broiler demand to take a bit of a stutter step, and demand may be beginning to plateau. How producers handle this plateau is going to be crucial to both short-term returns and long-term survival. The supply of true artisanal goods always lies in the hands of the producer, and that kind of control must extend beyond numbers to include quality and the image of both the product and the producer. If this plateauing continues it will not be safely resolved by the time-honored and nearly always wrong approach taken by those in production agriculture in the past. It is not the time to dig in, produce more, and try to fight for pennies in the marketplace. To profit from pennies you have to invest millions, if not billions. The example to follow, I believe, lies in one of the valleys of California, but not the Imperial or the San Joaquin. Rather it is to Napa Valley where poultry producers, all farmers actually, should be looking now. They should be producing farm goods equated with fine wines in the marketplace and building farms in the enduring nature and with the high regard reserved for the more legendary vineyards.

No, the brown egg is not the perfect food; there is no manna this side of the Jordan. In fact, I believe the white-shelled egg from a more natural system of production is already rising to challenge it. It is produced by a large number of breeds, many of which are more productive and less costly to maintain than the larger framed brown egg–laying breeds that are most commonly in use. Breeds like the Leghorn have smaller space requirements and consume substantially less feed per dozen of eggs produced.

As interest in white-shelled eggs begins to grow, consumers should become open to other egg options such as bantam and duck eggs on the table. What will almost certainly continue is this desire for distinctive, locally produced food items that are more than just commodities produced in high volume for the least cost in unending uniformity. One of the real first human freedoms enjoyed in the New World was the access to meat; the deer and the game birds did not belong to any king.

One of the earliest instances of commerce within the New World was the trade in livestock between the Pilgrims and the slightly later arrivals, the Puritans. Thus, when you consider the early significance of the "cow trader," much of history begins to make a bit more sense. Jokes aside, all of that livestock, including the feathered kind, was locally produced and had been bred up to the challenges and the resources of that new land. Local production and sustainability was shaping American agriculture from its very earliest times.

Columbus made landfall in the New World in 1492, as every schoolboy and girl knows. By the 1540s turkey was valued table fare during the holiday season in England. History does not record who ate the first egg taken from a Junglefowl's nest, nor the argument that led up to it. ("You eat it" "No, you eat it." "I'm not eating it." "You found it." "Yeah, so?" "Well I saw where it came from and I'm not eating it.") Still, we know that poultry, eggs, and even poultry fat anchor virtually every major cuisine around the world. And consumers are coming into the U.S. marketplace in ever greater numbers asking for very specific poultry varieties and products.

What began with brown-shelled eggs and range broilers is growing in magnitude. Egg and poultry meat production will probably never be completely wrenched from the hands of factory farming, but at long last opportunities are opening for producers on the human scale with poultry of varieties and forms that consumers can't or don't feel comfortable buying from the factory farm system. It is also production based on the concepts of elite, premium-valued and priced items. Demand for guineas, geese, ducklings, and the like has never been great in this country and that has to, I believe, be considered a good thing. Those who want them know them to not be readily available, and that scarcity factor thus gives them added value.

Factory farming is a high-volume process; it cannot afford to gear up for a product with modest levels of demand. You cannot buy lamb nuggets, for example. Nor can factory farming and big box stores come easily to bear on artisanal and local food production. As I write this you can buy organic food items at even the smallest, most rural Walmart stores in Missouri. It took time for that to happen, but when demand reached a certain point the large producers saw that market and found the means to come in on it in their typically heavy-handed manner.

Now, if you were to become the local producer of larger French guineas or Emden geese of exceptional quality or White Holland roasting turkeys to go along with well-bred Delaware or New Hampshire broilers, you are going to draw attention but little or no competition. You will be operating in a manner similar to that of a producer of pedigreed cattle or horses; you are a producer of foundation stock (and all that that term means) and consumables of a most select nature.

Over the years I have also been accused of a bias toward purebreds, both in poultry and hoofed stock, and that I will not deny. At the basest of levels, purebreds come with a readily identifiable presence and existing level of interest that often easily converts to demand. If you've never been on a farm or ranch in your life but have seen just one or two cowboy movies you know that white-faced Hereford cattle are the good stuff.

I have raised both Buff Plymouth Rock and Buff Wyandotte chickens over the years, but after saying no over and over again to the question "Are they Buff Orpingtons?" I finally went into the Buff Orpington business. I'm willing to bet good money that many who asked me that question at different farmers' markets couldn't tell the difference between a Buff Orpington and a Buff Hoot Owl, but they had heard that name applied to buff-feathered chickens often enough that it stuck with them.

During the golden era of U.S. poultry production, from roughly 1880 to 1950, the rural scene was dominated by small farm flocks and their owners who were, almost to a man and woman, poultry breeders. They were breeding the birds that set performance records that still stand and raised the image of the chicken from a lowly dunghill fowl to the chicken in every pot message that came to symbolize the good life in the United States.

Essential to the advancement of poultry keeping now is the arrival on the scene of those willing to take up the role of the farmer/breeder anew. The missing piece for the consumer in this poultry renaissance has been hard information, people to answer their sincere questions, still their concerns, and be responsive to them. And for multipliers it has been the need for seedstock that breeds true, for leaders that are pointing the way to an even better future with better bred and performing birds, and for ways to build upon and reinforce the current positive image that exists. All of that will come from a cadre of real-world thinkers, hands-on producers with a mind-set that is eons old and is expressed simply as doing all that is needed for "the good of the breed."

When asked to speak on poultry matters I spark questions and hard looks in a simple manner. I ask first that all who are under the age of forty will raise their hands. Then I will tell them that they have probably never seen a Rhode Island Red hen or a really good Barred Plymouth Rock rooster. For the last half century or a bit more, poultry stock production has been dominated by hybrid varieties, birds bred to fit confinement facilities, and "industrial" purebreds that have been bred to somewhat look the part. As the interest in heritage breeds rose anew, real concerns about their genetic integrity began to emerge. It's hard to pick up a hatchery catalog now or scroll the Internet pop-up hatcheries and find one that isn't touting its heritage-bred stock. This is symptomatic of the shenanigans that all but destroyed the exotics sector in agriculture a couple of decades ago. A breed or variety gets hot, selling prices spiral upward in what is termed a "breeders' market," and a lot of poorly bred and even some falsely represented birds get sold. Everyone wants a few of whatever the hot breed of the moment is, and there are some people ready to sell birds that at least vaguely look the part. What results is a lot of tainted gene pools, a breed possibly left in shambles, a lot of folks disappointed and turned off to poultry keeping, and another setback for the whole of the poultry community.

Breeders specializing in varieties that caught fire a few years ago are now finding that they must, to borrow a cowhand's term, go back and relick the calf. They have to pinpoint anew the gene sources that remain true, weed out the junk with minimal finger-pointing, and begin a whole new program of reeducation about a particular breed.

Your warning radar should go off whenever you encounter what are supposed to be purebred hatchlings at bargain-basement prices, stock for sale at places that normally sell motor oil and bale wrap, or encounter hatcheries or suppliers that pop up overnight offering dozens of breeds and varieties. A lot of the very best breeders have made a lifetime of work developing just a single breed.

A lifetime of raising livestock has shown me that learning to raise livestock takes a lifetime. There is always something new to learn, but well-bred birds seldom vary much beyond the type and role for which they were initially developed. Over the years I have owned Wyandottes of many colors and patterns; it is a breed with which I have some history and identity. Their type and value are shaped by the roles for which they were developed: to be fair layers, to grow reasonably well, to have good cold-weather tolerance, and to perform well in simpler housing.

I was schooled, if you will, in the purebred hog trade. Prices per head there were and are many times higher than with poultry, but the groundwork had been set by an earlier generation of poultry producers that pioneered the concept of selective breeding for improved performance. You kept good records, learned to evaluate animals at every stage of life, culled hard, evaluated every type trend with a cold eye, bred always for hardiness and fertility, and learned quickly that the most important of all economic traits is live young in good numbers.

In the first half of the twentieth century there were a great many aspects of poultry keeping that are missing now. There were breed- and even variety-specific publications and breeder groups, numerous publications addressing the art and science of poultry production including market reporting, poultry exhibitions in major venues such as Madison Square Garden in New York City, and a great many poultry marketing outlets with buyers based in nearly every small town. There was an overall image of professionalism to the poultry community. I have been to numerous poultry events where a pair of very rare turkeys, a handful of well-bred pullets, or an exceptional pair of geese have been purchased only to go live in what is essentially a feathered menagerie in someone's backyard. You are not preserving a breed when you pluck birds from an already small population and then shut them away to never reproduce.

Not everyone is cut out to be a breeder of poultry or beef cattle or racehorses. Still, those in the role of breeder/farmer are needed the most. If you want just a few brown- or green-shelled eggs or to raise just a holiday turkey or two as an abject lesson for the kids or to have some green-headed ducks on the pond, then buy from the most common industrial birds. Or seek out those with good birds, pay up for their seconds (we all have them), and know that your money is going to help the cause of good poultry and family farms.

I have made my share of jokes about all of those "Other White Meat" bumper stickers and John Deere caps, but we in poultry production now do need a few accessories like these to bolster our public identity and affirm the role we are attempting to play in society. In the first half of the last century, poultrymen wore soft caps and then engineer-style headgear. Feed companies had scores of poultry-themed logos, and the *Poultry Tribune* was read in more places than the Sunday newspaper. I looked for the better part of five years before finding a belt buckle with a rooster on it. I cannot help but wonder what it would mean to have an item of clothing that gave poultry producers the recognition that cowboy hats give cattlemen and creased bill caps give hog producers. And no, I don't mean a pink t-shirt that reads "Have you kissed your chicken?"

The history of poultry keeping shows the names of many high-profile breeders associated with the development and propagation of various poultry breeds and varieties. The more familiar names were generally associated with large fowl chicken varieties, but, for example, there are numerous accounts from early in the twentieth century of those developing duck breeds that are egg layers of exceptional merit.

I have a good friend in Alabama who has been linebreeding from the same line of "belt-buckle high" Emden geese for decades. He transported them over great distances as his family made various moves. They are special to him and in turn have given him some recognition and identity as a producer of exceptional goose stock. Becoming identified with a breed or variety can become the basis for a business venture. Big white geese or vividly colored Royal Palm turkeys strutting in a front pasture will bring attention to a farm or smallholding. People will often stop in with questions and offers to buy

Participation in the local farmers' market and work with 4-Hers made us some of the local go-to folks for chicken questions and needs. It is a position similar to the one we had for thirty-five plus years when supplying Duroc breeding stock to other small farmers in our area.

In recent years the poultry business has taken up some shortcuts and fast routes to production in volume that perhaps weren't as carefully thought out as they should have been. Hybrid chicken hens have been developed for a one-and-done season of egg laying. They produce a rather large egg in proportion to body size and have been bred to a "layer type" deemed ideal for factory farming concepts, generally a hybridized form of the White Leghorn scaled down for life in the laying cage and with its genetic variability reduced by over 50 percent. It is an assembly-line chicken for assembly-line egg production. The Broadbreasted turkey in Bronze and White varietals has emerged as a poorly animated, ball-shaped mass of white meat. Those massive, misshapen turkeys are equally short lived. Sadly, they are so misshapen that they are no longer able to even breed naturally. A good political cartoon would be one of those monstrous toms surrounded by a number of turkey hens and carrying a placard that reads, "Where are those animal rights people when you really need them?"

There have long been size concerns with meat-bred chickens and even some birds bred über-large for the show room. Likewise there are some lines of Pekins and other meat ducks that have been bred to a massive scale. The push to ever larger meat birds has been done more to increase output from the killing floor and the processing floor than for any other reason. This is to maximize output from areas where the meat industry has to pay hourly wages and provide benefits. This kind of poundage can and does depress markets, and these super-large birds only have fullest value where the meat is restructured into things for which it was never really intended. Turkey hot dogs and bologna, anyone? The average family with its 2.5 children has little need for a forty-five-pound tom turkey at Christmas even if Santa and all eight reindeer stay over for dinner.

Along with usage concerns, these larger fowl have brought flavor and texture issues with them as well. Not only does the meat of the Cornish-X broiler not look like chicken, it doesn't taste like chicken either. And that is something that turtle and even alligator meat can manage!

Excepting a handful of instances, these alternative poultry varieties were never big-ticket items for farmers and smallholders. They were generally held in smallish numbers and fitted in and around other, larger ventures in the individual enterprise mixes.

Most of these birds that we kept were held in small breeding populations: often a couple of trios, a few pairs, or one or two males and a breeding pen of four to six females. Due to the fecund nature of most poultry varieties even a bare handful of females can produce several score of hatchlings in a breeding season. You can place a hundred broilers pretty quickly within your immediate circle; with twenty roasting geese you might have fewer options than the owner of a litter of mongrel puppies that need new homes.

My friend from Alabama with the good Emden geese, Neal Gray, has found his niche with the production from one or two trios. There are seasonal aspects to the production and marketing of all of these birds, but they have to be fed and tended twelve months out of the year.

I recall one fellow that popped up at our local farmers' market a single time many years ago. He had bought some Pekin ducklings early that year and, as can happen, he had a brief flush of egg laying from them in mid-fall. Unable to resist the temptation he placed a good lot of those eggs in an incubator. And there he was at an early December farmers' market with ducklings, lots and lots of ducklings, to sell. Nothing is cuter than a little duck, but no one wanted them riding in the little cars of electric trains encircling the family Christmas tree. It was a hard lesson for him to learn. A harder one still awaited him as he tried to find starter rations suitable for baby ducks available at that late date in the year.

Efforts are under way to expand marketing opportunities for alternative poultry varieties, but most producers will be selling on rather localized markets for some time to come. Such markets can absorb only modest amounts of product before going tilt. Through numbers offered and the quality present in those numbers, the producer can have substantial control over these markets, the prices paid, and how demand is developed. Our local producers' group has developed a monthly market known for the variety and the rarity of the poultry breeds offered there. As one member of the American Livestock Breeds Conservancy said, "You people trade in breeds most people only read about in magazines."

Job one in marketing is to develop a presence in the marketplace as one who can be relied upon and who offers high-quality production. The good birds eat no more than the other kind—often less—and they always sell for more. And where numbers are small, there is no excuse for them not being good.

That thinking set me to a task many years ago that has shaped my beliefs on how to farm ever since. For many years, each spring and fall our mailbox would fill with the sale catalogs for swine breeder auctions. A breeder, on that one night, might offer two hundred–plus hogs at auction. As I really studied those catalogs it began to emerge that the best performing and highest selling animals in those offerings generally came from a single family and often just a handful of matings. Though there might be a great many females in the breeding herd, a much smaller, more select group was producing a greater share of the overall sales. Granted, these more elite individuals were getting a bit better care and more attention, but the returns they produced justified it. And they were subsidizing the rest of the herd and the investment needed to care for it. A small core of exceptional individuals was bearing the costs for a producer to farm big. You had to be good to have the numbers, but you really didn't have to have the numbers to be good and profitable. The advantage of scale quickly vanishes in the face of the edge afforded by quality output.

I have heard this conclusion expressed another way in an anecdote frequently told in poultry circles. Two different producers of the same breed of turkey are asked to fill an order for fifteen very good poults. One producer then puts twenty-five eggs in the incubator and the other sets seventy-five to hatch.

Either one of these might be termed a fairly typical response and both have a lot to say about the mind-set and the thinking processes that are going into poultry and other types of livestock production now. The producer setting the larger number of eggs probably keeps a larger number of birds. There are, no doubt, some very good birds in the flock, but that bird producer knows his base and that it produces in inconsistent ways. He has come to rely on producing in volume to get the numbers, and he can then skim the cream. And, hopefully, he has a large family that loves turkey to deal with the rest.

The other producer has put in the time and the base inputs to create a small, tight flock that produces quality offspring in a most consistent manner. Not every hatchling produced can go on to be a purple-ribbon winner, but when bred from a good base that has proven itself they have a level of dependability that both builds markets and pares costs to produce. And that does not happen overnight unless you lay down the long green needed to buy out an established flock being dispersed.

Simply, if you have the good stuff you can get the job done with far fewer numbers and less fuss and feathers. Now the good stuff can't be had on the cheap, is sometimes quite hard to find, often entails a few false starts, and may have to be built up on the home holding one good bird at a time. I've watched the most veteran of producers arrive at a bird market or auction and work through each coop there very carefully. Generally, they have much better stock at home, but they are always open to the prospect and possibility of finding that one bird that can move their own flock forward.

You also have to resist the temptation to get too far out there, to build the numbers beyond what your market, your facilities, or your skill set can support. And, along with too many numbers, you can come upon breeds and varieties that, while they catch the eye, are really not a good fit for your farm or smallholding. There is a variety of goose, the Sebastopol, with a most striking appearance; many of its feathers look like they have been given a permanent wave. Compared to most goose breeds, however, it is less hardy, lays poorly, may require added housing, and is rather short-lived. I recall the experiences of a business associate with breeds like the Sebastapol. He was beginning a hatchery venture and traveled widely and invested extensively in seedstock for such rare varieties as Sebastapol geese and White Faverolle chickens. He expended a great deal of time and capital in such acquisitions, met with limited demand for and reduced production from such birds, and he soon abandoned the hatchery venture entirely.

Long ago Dad cautioned me that if I were ever to bring in anything to grow on our farm from five hundred miles away I had better be prepared to haul it back over every one of those five hundred miles to get it sold. That old, plain-Jane Beltsville White turkey, Brown Chinese goose, Pearl guinea, or White Rock hen still makes a lot of sense if it comes from a well-bred flock and is backed by a breeder/producer that knows his or her stuff.

In the feeder cattle trade there is a term, "reputation cattle." It does not refer to a specific breed nor feeding program, but to cattle from a farm and a man or woman who does things the right way, takes the pains to do the little things that boost quality, believes in the stock and the business, has been there for the long haul, and can be trusted. We need a lot of "reputation" feathered stock, we need it soon, and we need it to last. You can't buy such a reputation, and it takes time to build one, lots of time. While it might seem like something of a nebulous term, reputation breeding is evident. It shows in the birds produced and the black ink on the ledger page.

How often have I seen newcomers start out with a breed or variety with all the bells and whistle of size, feathering, and coloration? Based on a picture or two in a catalog, they will take on a breed or variety with such challenges that even veteran breeders shy away from it. If your heart is set on such a breed, go with it. All need more breeders. Just keep in mind that your wishes and interests may not convert to demand and sales.

A recent farm publication noted for its features on alternative farm ventures ran an article on a farmer diversifying with the addition of a few pairs of Impeyan pheasants of his farming mix. They are four-hundred-dollar-a-pair birds that produce just eight to twelve eggs per year, but their vivid colors (some call them the "nine-colored bird") and rarity has created something of a demand for them. They are probably birds only for the most dedicated of aviculturists, and their marketability hinges on them being seen to build sales. They did make their way into the pages of a major agribusiness magazine that also had articles on massive grain carts and refits for grain hauling semi-rigs. When you are presented with an opportunity to promote you do have to take it. And if these birds catch fire it may mean opportunities for no more than a handful of breeders in each state at best.

Get too far out there with very rare genetics or challenging birds to breed to a standard and you will be too much on your own. There are birds now that can be acquired just a handful of hatchlings at a time or only as hatching eggs. Replacement stock and much-needed advice and support may be a half continent or more away. While black- and white-feathered birds may sometimes not sell as readily as some other colors, they are generally quite dependable in that aspect of their breeding. Hot colors, popular colors of the moment, are generally much more complex to manage. Chocolate and lavender birds are very complex in their creation; recessive genetic factors may be at play, and there will be real problems with keeping those colors breeding true and of the proper intensity. Always beware of lines that require separate male and female breeding lines, and there is a bantam color pattern or two produced only by mating together birds of two different color patterns.

There are a great many seeking out "blue" (actually a sort of gray) poultry. While that color has been around for generations, there are still a great many who don't understand how it manifests itself. A blue-hued bird mated to another blue bird will produce roughly 50 percent blue offspring, 25 percent black offspring, and 25 percent light or splash-colored young. Each color phase has value and can be used to maintain and even intensify blue coloring, but it is one more big factor in flock management.

The other day at a local poultry event, I saw a trio of White Plymouth Rocks that were brought in from several states away and offered for sale. They sold almost immediately and drew many more inquiries and offers to buy before being packed away by their new owner. Now, you can't get any more plain vanilla than a White Plymouth Rock. Those birds were solid to Plymouth Rock type, were well-grown and correct to size, and, as we say in Missouri, shone like a new dime at the bottom of a pail of spring water. They were good enough that people confronted with a great many different breeds that day quickly found them. And they did their own selling job just by standing correctly in their cage and looking like good birds should. Not long ago I saw a young pair of Brown African geese bring a hundred dollar bill, with no counteroffer, because they stood out as good representatives of that breed. They would form a very good base from which to begin a flock, should produce viable eggs for a decade and more, and, with good care, would go on to create a lasting farm venture that would have been cheap to start even at that fifty-dollar-per-bird price.

Sometimes, especially with some of the lesser and older breeds, you will have to make the start with what is at hand or is most easily accessible. Several times over the years I have bought a pair or trio of birds knowing that they were lacking in some areas, but they were what I could find at the moment and were the tangible symbol of the work I needed to do and had best start doing. It was a start, and sometimes the only way in is to build numbers from what you have, as they will breed close to the average in type, and then cull hard to get down to the best. To that end you must not succumb to barn blindness but see the birds before you as they really are.

Once upon a time in poultry circles there was a very active trade in what were termed "stud males." These were males of exceptional type, backed by performance breeding, and came from flocks with a highly regarded reputation. Their use would boost flock performance in a manner somewhat akin to what is seen with heterosis, or hybrid vigor. They were used to create outcross matings, and their fullest effect was felt in daughters and granddaughters going back into the home flock.

Quite often now small flock breeders are following a line- or family-based breeding program and may close a flock for several years. Such linebreeding will bring out the best and the worst in livestock, and the producer must carefully monitor and select for vigor, size, and continuing reproductive performance. Problems may manifest in the form of reduced fertility, slower hatching times and/or defects in the hatchlings (curled toes, crossed beaks, etc.). When it is necessary to bring new blood into such a line, it is generally done with the introduction of one or two females, preferably full sisters. Some will even seek out females with a similar genetic background to the flock. These birds are set up in a separate side mating. They are penned away from other birds and mated to the very best senior male from the existing flock. Their eggs and then their hatchlings are given separate identifying marks and then grown out under great scrutiny. If the mating has been found to work, to "nick," a handful of the very best pullets will be retained. The breeder will then breed them into the main body of the flock slowly, carefully following the course and performance of their offspring.

It's hard to pinpoint when I got to the point where I felt I was doing things the way they should be done. Sometimes I think I am not there yet. Some would say it was the time I turned down an offer of one hundred dollars on a young trio of White Rocks, and my good wife, Phyllis, let me not only live but return home with her. To me it was when I upgraded to a larger incubator and the other equipment needed to make ever more controlled and verifiable matings. Shortly after that I also began a course of paring breed and variety numbers and am at last getting down to a sense of the more manageable.

I have seen people do the truly daunting: getting good hatches of goose eggs in Styrofoam incubators, hatching peafowl eggs under banty hens, or maintaining large numbers of breeds and varieties on quite small parcels of land. A loose rooster can cost you two precious weeks at the height of the breeding season, and I know of no way to command a hen to go broody when dearly bought eggs arrive.

To have a business, even a small one, you have to be businesslike in the ways that really matter. We store some feed in an old deep freeze that quit working decades ago, and our incubator and first brooder are in a garden shed our nephew built in high school. A couple of our smaller breeding groups eat and drink from half-gallon tuna fish cans my wife brings home from her work. We will spend top dollar for breeding stock, don't stint on feed, subscribe to a number of poultry publications, use several methods to identify and track individual birds, and we're committed to farming our feathered stock just like we did the hogs, cattle, and sheep. When it comes to livestock production of any sort I cannot emphasize enough the importance of producer mind-set.

For many decades small flock poultry production had just sort of trundled along well off the radar. Individual birds were perceived to be of very little value; for most people they had become an out-of-sight, out-of-mind thing, and when poultry meat and products arrived in the home it was rather like the television signals of thirty years ago. There were very few choices, there was no pizzazz, and the TV dinner was paving the way for the free-form, rather tasteless bits and strips of chicken and turkey with which most contend now. People now have to be told that a duck isn't a turkey isn't a quail isn't a squab. And, most importantly, a factory-farmed chicken broiler is none of the above.

❦

An operation working with one or more of these alternative poultry varieties will have to largely carve out its own structure and identity. Some producers have been trying to pair the concepts embodied in a smaller herd of pedigreed hoof stock and a micro-hatchery. It might be described as a sort of laid-back retail presence. One of these poultry ventures might be used to capitalize on labor not needed elsewhere on the farm, to even and extend cash flow, to help draw and hold customers to the output of a particular farm or smallholding, to capitalize on producer skills and interests, and to more fully utilize of farm resources.

The seasonal aspects of poultry production have been fitted rather tidily into farming patterns in many parts of the United States. The birds are often started in the early part of the year, ahead of much of the field work. The output from some alternative poultry ventures can be marketed steadily throughout the year, and other times the marketing falls in summer or late fall when more labor is available and there may be a bit of a flat line to income flow.

For some, poultry production has had an image as something done by children and farmwives for pin money. Yes, poultry ventures once relied upon all family members for labor, but they were very real contributors to a farm's earning potential. Egg and fryer money were grocery money and much more for a great many farm families. Open a text from the first half of the last century, such as any of the classic books by Morley A. Jull, and you will see farmers fully engaged in poultry production, breeding, and marketing. It is not numbers but mind-set that makes poultry keeping a poultry business. Do you want to sell a couple dozen turkeys a year, or do you want to market fifty heritage-bred birds of exceptional merit and deserving of a premium price and place in the market?

Birds that are worth more and reflect well on the producer do not just happen. Do you know which tom in the flock is of the best type? Which hens are producing the most eggs and then hatchlings? How much does it cost to produce a hatchling poult? A finished turkey ready for harvest? How old are they at harvest? If you are selling each bird for less than it costs to produce, selling a couple dozen each year in no way helps to "recover some of the costs" of keeping a few turkeys or ducks or pheasants.

The birds before you now are often little more than shadows of what they were over a half century ago. The feed, equipment, and production methods are all better, but the birds themselves have been largely stuck in time, slipping in numbers until just recently.

A box of hatchlings can be the beginning of a lifelong, a family business, a career and a calling. It can also be a source of great disappointment and aggravation, but that, too, is shaped by mind-set. A friend recently told me of giving twenty-five dollars apiece for a half-dozen (all the breeder would sell) as-hatched chicks of a rather rare breed of chicken. One hundred fifty dollars plus shipping is a lot to pay for a half-dozen peeps, but they will give him a second breeding line, added marketing potential, and were a needed step in him becoming an established breeder in an area where poultry demand is strong but that breed is not present.

Once the feathers are removed, it currently matters little whether the turkey on the serving tray was a Slate, a Bourbon Red or a traditional Bronze. As things unfold and knowledge is gained, it may emerge that there are some varietal differences in turkey meat, or strains within the same variety could have some differences. Five or six generations of thoughtful, selective breeding—roughly five to six years with most poultry species—can make some very marked differences in a breeding group or farm flock. One of the major costs of poultry production—feed efficiency—can be addressed through selective breeding, as can egg production, growth rate, soundness, durability, and many more factors, all essential to successful production. There have been massive tomes written on poultry breeding, some that would challenge a graduate student to read and follow.

On the family farm or smallholding, an old, old law of genetics—breed the best to the best (in type and performance)—is still a pretty good plan of operation. One of the beauties of working with smaller numbers is that the best performers quickly and clearly emerge, and their path through the flock is fairly easily tracked. On the other hand, if a poor bird is used for breeding the damage emerges quickly and is generally widespread due to the smaller numbers involved.

Buy the American Poultry Association's *American Standard of Perfection* and maybe a couple of older editions from decades back when purebred poultry were one of the pillars of the family farm. They provide the yardsticks to measure type and structure and were drawn up by breeder/producers who valued and depended upon working birds. And always temper your book learning with what you know to be true of your farm, your environment, your market, and yourself.

I don't believe that you can boil animal breeding down to just simple numbers and indexes. A bird with a coefficient of 116 percent of the flock average for egg laying sounds impressive until you learn that the flock average is just ten eggs per female.

A bird cannot be whisked from a controlled environment facility to a more natural environment without setbacks. It has been bred for generations to perform nowhere else. Nor should you expect immediate results from a bird plucked from one climate and taken across the country to another. They need time to adapt and adjust. While on the subject of adaptation, allow me to quote again from some of my old-school livestock mentors, "Blue-ribbon winners seldom make good parents, but they can often be crackerjack grandmas and grandpas." What is meant by that is that the good genetic potential prizewinning birds represent must come to be fully understood on their new home base and become better melded with the breeding program there. By the second generation, the strengths they carried have found their niche and adapted to that farm's environment, which is shaped by everything from soil content to the "bug" mix.

You have to know what to keep and what to let go. I say, only half in jest, that before buying that first trio or box of hatchlings, buy a couple of cookbooks on how to utilize them in many different ways. I field a lot of questions about the super-large breeds of chicken, but many producers quickly turn away from them once they learn how long it takes for some of these birds to develop and how much they eat while doing it. For some birds it may take a full year before the final culling steps. Some species were developed to be meat birds, but meat birds for a very different era. It takes time to grow out a large frame and then to put on the desired finish and feathering. A well-bred Toulouse goose may take three years to reach full sexual maturity.

To some it might sound like I have presented some rather contradictory thoughts here, but while a small investment in a seasonal poultry venture may offer the fastest turnaround on investment of nearly any made in production agriculture to get a true, quality-based poultry business up and running will take time and patience and plenty of both.

Taking a poultry pursuit to the next step, to making a business endeavor of it, requires a level of investment that many had not considered and that others thought would never be made again.

To do the best job, you need good tools, which are those that 1) give the venture a better and more polished image, 2) enable the producer to do things in the most timely manner, 3) give the producer a better self-image and inspire him or her to do a better job, and 4) improve the quality of output from the enterprise.

In a poultry venture the key investment (after seedstock) and the hub from which all production will flow is the incubator. Incubation is mostly science, a bit of art, and leavened by a nice little dollop of luck. We have had years of very poor hatching rates follow by years where we have run out of places to put hatchlings. We have had young bird crops that tilted very heavily toward youngsters of one sex or the other. We have survived power outages, hot spells, cold springs, and once having to relocate a loaded incubator over forty miles down the road. As noted earlier, many small-scale producers still rely on at least some natural incubation. I am in the process right now of filling an order for some Buff Orpingtons that still retain at least some tendency to go broody.

Most go first into artificial incubation on the cheap with a small table-top incubator, possibly one of the old, round, metal units that have been gathering dust in farmhouse attics for decades, or perhaps one of the square, largely Styrofoam models that fill farm supply store shelves every year around Easter. A real advancement, a milestone of sorts, comes when a producer steps up to a unit of larger capacity, generally a cabinet model incubator. It is not always a necessary step, and I have seen producers of some scale continuing to operate with a half-dozen or more of the small units humming away all together. Need for greater volume, the desire for an easier-to-operate unit, or the need for earlier hatching are factors that move most producers to consider and then invest in a larger incubator. Small incubators, even the cabinet models, are rather like older tractors or a vintage pickup. Each will have its own little quirks of operation, and the producer has to get in sync with them to generate the best possible production from the unit.

The choices are many. I have seen high-tech twenty-egg models push the five hundred dollar range; bare-bones Styrofoam still retails for a bit over thirty bucks, and a new cabinet model with about three hundred–egg capacity retails for between six and seven hundred. Used units are generally widely available and range in condition from those that have been used only once to those in need of a complete rebuilding.

Fortunately, a strong market has developed for incubator parts, and even parts for those decades-old Sears and Brower round, metal units can be bought. I have a friend that has restored an old redwood Leahy incubator that was actually being used as a coffee table before he acquired it. Hereabouts a lot of folks have found good buys in cabinet models that were designed and sold for ostrich and emu eggs back when those markets were booming. Though having one fewer rack they will fit a good numbers of eggs in species-specific trays.

Good hatching performance, however, begins long before the eggs enter the incubator, long before they are laid, actually. Here are some thoughts on incubation success that begin in the poultry yard:

1. The breeders should be in good health and condition, free of internal and external parasites, provided with quality feedstuffs and clean drinking water, and should have grown well for their age. Many hatcheries now use birds for the breeding flock that were just hatchlings the year before. This is done to pare costs of operation by not carrying breeders through a molt and a winter season. Still, there are old hands that insist that eggs for hatching should not be saved from a bird's first year of lay. They reason that eggs should be saved only from birds that have proven themselves good producers of a durable nature. Also, the longer a bird is on the farm or smallholding, the greater the level of natural immunity will be built into them and passed on to the young they produce. They will have benefited from the longer exposure to the "bug" mix on that site. We have noted measurably greater survival rates and growth from second generation and beyond hatchlings over first generation from new stock hatchlings produced here.

2. Even species that don't lay great numbers of eggs will benefit from being fed breeder/layer rations with higher levels of nutrient-dense protein. They should be gradually changed over to these hotter rations at least four to six weeks before eggs are to be retained for hatching.

   I have seen poultrymen tweak breeder rations in a number of ways to get fertile eggs earlier in the year and to maintain egg production and fertility in the face of stress-causing factors such as extreme heat. Most endeavor to increase protein levels by offering richer feedstuffs (game bird feed, catfish feed, pet food, or even bits of hamburger). Some will add products to the drinking water, ranging from simple vitamin/electrolyte products to their own tonic mixes of red vinegar, garlic, red pepper, and more.

   Make any such changes or additions gradually, and don't get too far out there. For example, I've heard tales of old cockfighters feeding things as exotic as gunpowder. The egg-as-a-hand-grenade is not a market to which you should aspire.

3. Eggs for incubation should be gathered several times each day, at least three to four times daily in very cold weather. Nests should be large enough and deep enough to accommodate the species

being kept: two feet by two feet by eight inches deep, at floor level for some of the larger species. Use nesting material that will provide a good cushion and also keep the eggs clean and dry. Inspect the nests often for evidence of vermin and to keep the nesting material clean and fresh. Each egg being considered for incubation should be inspected closely. Candle each egg before placing it in the incubator to detect any fine cracks or shell checkering. Discard such eggs as they can spoil in the heat of the incubator and harm the eggs around them. Overly dirty or stained eggs should be discarded. Some dried materials can be removed from the eggshell by light scraping with a dull blade or light sanding with fine grit sandpaper. A badly stained egg or one with a fine crack could spawn bacteria that kill a whole hatch.

Eggs can be stored for up to ten to twelve days prior to incubation, small-end down, if held properly. Best results will be achieved with eggs stored for no more than seven to eight days. Larger incubators will accommodate the weekly egg production from a pretty fair number of birds. For best results store the eggs where temperatures range between forty-five to sixty degrees Fahrenheit. They should be given a slight turn several times each day to keep the air cells from sticking. Eggs laid in very warm weather can enter a state of pre-incubation. They may have reduced hatchability or hatch twenty-four to thirty-six hours earlier than expected.

4. Know that there is a seasonality to egg production and hatchability that is based first on the increasing length of daylight hours. Increasing temperatures will also have an effect on certain birds with origins in warmer climes. Sumatras, for example, are traditional warm-weather layers.

5. Match male and female numbers correctly. Too many males in the breeding pen or group can result in fighting, incomplete matings, and reduced fertility. It may also adversely affect the condition of the females. Early in the year carefully monitor the condition of the breeding males for signs of a strong libido and completed matings.

6. When a fertility problem is detected, it may be necessary to replace males or break up matings that simply aren't performing to expectations. Keeping a couple of extra breeding males and a backup pair or breeding trio is cheap insurance to prevent the loss of an entire breeding year.

I have to say that I have never owned any two small incubators that performed in the same way and could be operated exactly the same. I've known producers to disagree on incubator brands, temperature settings, and even where to position the unit for best results. Most have them sitting in a back bedroom, garage, or well-made outbuilding. It is best to position them where air temperatures can be maintained at a fairly consistent range, and best results come at around sixty to sixty-five degrees Fahrenheit around the cabinet or casement. Try to avoid temperature fluctuations of more than ten to fifteen degrees around the units. The intense heat of 2012 took a real toll on incubators set up in outbuildings in the Midwest and South.

Here are a few points on incubator operation that we have learned over the years:

1. Before being placed into use each year the units should be thoroughly cleaned and disinfected. It should be done after their last use in the year. They should be turned on and allowed to run for several days to ascertain steady operating temperature before any eggs are placed in them. Those units that use wafer thermostats should have those wafers replaced before each hatching season. A defective wafer may appear flattened, fully expanded, badly tarnished, or somewhat tan in color. Failure can occur just about any time.

   Trays and racks should be cleaned and disinfected after every hatching. The turner should be tested before any eggs are placed. To determine turner activity, inspect the unit at different times of the day to verify that the eggs are being repositioned. If you check at the same times every day, the turner will always be in the same position.

   Empty, partially filled, and filled incubators will operate differently and give different temperature and humidity readings. A filled incubator will do a better job of holding heat, often give better hatches, and will probably be more efficient to operate.

2. It's very important to monitor the humidity of your unit. In the Midwest and South you will often hear producers discuss "dry hatches." The spring and summer in these regions can have very high natural humidity levels, so the producers do not provide additional water in the incubator as the air entering the unit is already quite humid. A very dry spring a while back took quite a toll on hatches here. Likewise, fast-moving fronts in succession can affect incubator operation. Just as there can be hatchability

and survival problems with too low a humidity level, hatchlings in too humid a unit with appear wet and spongy and will be slow to their feet. A low humidity in the unit will reduce hatch rates, young may die in the shell, and others may pip the egg but die before emerging.

Hatchlings that are alive and struggling to emerge from the shell are a real challenge. Efforts to pick away the shell can cause injury or the umbilicus to rupture and the peep to bleed to death. If the emerging hatchling appears to be drying out, use an eye-dropper to release a few drops of warm water (possibly drawn from the humidifier tank) into the egg around the struggling youngster. A few producers have reported some success dipping such hatchlings and the eggs constraining them into the humidifier reservoir and then placing them back into the hatcher.

Two points here on some troubleshooting:

a. Where water is drawn through tubing or misters into the cabinet, monitor all flows carefully to be sure they aren't being restricted by mineralization. This has been real problem with the hard water supplies here in northern Missouri. Hatcheries have been known to operate a water softener ahead of the water line supplying the misters in their large incubators. On small units with lines supplied by gravity tanks, use softened water where available and replace the lines often as they become discolored.

b. In small tabletop units where the reservoir is beneath the eggs in small tracks in the bottom case, there can be a problem with reduced humidity. To counter this, cut strips of sponge to fit into the reservoirs and extend upward toward the eggs. The sponges will wick more water up toward the eggs and are simple and inexpensive to change out often to maintain sanitation in the unit.

3. Incubators should be positioned away from drafts and out of direct sunlight. Airflow and humidity in the incubator can be controlled somewhat either by repositioning the small metal flaps on the back of cabinet models or by taking out or popping back in the small plastic buttons in the top half of a tabletop unit. If those button tabs become lost, do not attempt to cover those small openings with strips of tape. When the adhesive on these is heated it can create atmosphere issues inside the unit.

4. The little units with their porous Styrofoam surfaces should be cleaned and disinfected after each hatch. Thoroughly air out the units after disinfection, as the disinfecting solutions can sometimes adversely affect hatching.

5. Enter the incubator no more than is absolutely necessary, do whatever has to be done quickly, close and completely seal the unit, and then closely monitor the temperature for a quick return to normal operating range. On cabinet units, old hands advise turning off the fan, where possible, before opening the unit. There will be less temperature loss as a result.

6. With the small Styrofoam models there are some tweaks that may improve hatches. Many will buy a new bottom unit at the start of each hatching season. It will be an expenditure of about fifteen dollars. They are often easier to replace than clean and may deteriorate after several uses and cleanings. Some now have plastic bottom liners that can be used for a few hatches and then discarded. Be sure to buy the correct liner for your unit model. Some producers will line the bottom of the unit with heavy aluminum foil. It should be positioned with the dull side up and should be replaced after every hatch. If possible, placing the idled units in direct sunlight for a day or two between uses will give them good exposure to the naturally disinfecting rays of the sun.

Not everyone is going to need a six hundred– or even a three hundred–egg incubator, but the incubator is one of the most crucial of tools in a poultry venture, whatever its size. The investment in a good unit is easily justifiable.

The renaissance in poultry keeping and the growing demand for premium, local, artisanal foods has returned the phrase "small poultry business" to popular use. It may involve just six heirloom turkeys, twenty purebred ducks of one of the rarer breeds, or a small flock of New Hampshire hens that produce broilers that taste like real chicken. Your goal with them should not be to become the next Tyson or Perdue but to help perpetuate a breed and a tradition of locally produced food that is one of the roots of the American lifestyle.

CHAPTER 8

More than a Fad
Keeping the Poultry Renaissance Alive

PHEASANT

A s diverse as these poultry species are, they all pose the same question to potential producers: What, ultimately, is to be done with them? To what role and level will they be restored? There is no fast food chain featuring goose nuggets. There are no rural buying stations for ducks or pigeons. Nor are there stockyards for creatures that cackle, squawk, quack, gobble, or honk. These birds have held on in a few places because there were weekly community or consignment auctions where you would find some feathered stock in the offering. In my youth there were any number of small towns with mercantiles or feed stores that also bought eggs, spent hens, spring and summer fryers, and just about anything else with feathers.

I can still remember walking around the by then long-abandoned poultry pens at the old Alderson Bros. mercantile in our little country town. They were soon to be torn down, but I had seen them filled with birds and crowded coops, piled atop each other on the loading dock awaiting the transport trucks. I had walked them often in the past looking for a bird of unusual variety or color to take back home. The birds were generally all played out but were nonetheless traces of what poultry production had once been in our part of Missouri and in most other states.

Some of this culture is coming back, although it is still as delicate as the last of the feathers that blew through those old holding pens in our little country town back in the sixties. A place to sell them—actually many places—are essential if these birds are going to continue in any form beyond a mere novelty. With the growing roles of direct marketing and local foods there must be meeting places for producers and consumers, points of education and information sharing, building points for a new infrastructure, and gates through which money and support can flow to build new flocks and sustain those already about the task of flock building.

Time and again, studies have revealed that the best way to improve the rural economy and the way of life there is simply to improve farmer income. A dollar spent with a farmer will turn nine to thirteen times before it leaves the immediate community. It will move up and down Main Street from the farmer to the feed store to the local diner to the hardware store to the mom and pop grocery. Direct marketing returns more of the selling price to the farmer/producer than any other form of marketing. It is also the marketing system with the greatest level of transparency as the farmer and the consumer have to meet face-to-face and strike a bargain over the actual item.

Poultry markets—and the whole of the livestock trade, actually—come under excessive and undue scrutiny every time a chicken sneezes in

China now. Yes, the Spanish flu epidemic of 1918 was a terrible thing; it was also nearly a hundred years ago and lifetimes away as far as medical developments are concerned. Dad would tell stories of having to tend his stricken family all alone at the age of eleven. Neighbors would bring food and what health measures were then available and leave them at their front gate. It was an act of great kindness, but my dad was also told that he ran the risk of being shot if he left their little farm before the disease had run its course.

Yes, some of those flus that have emerged recently in the East have had a porcine or an avian link. Sometimes quite a faint one. Public health care there is not what it is in more developed parts of the world. Generally, in those regions the people live in close proximity to their birds, often even sleeping directly above them to protect them from theft and predation. Cockfighting continues in many parts of these regions. A practice in the fighting pit in many areas is to catch up a bird with head or chest wounds and, using the human mouth, suck out the clotting blood from airways before setting the bird back down to continue the fight. There, too, cooking methods are not always the best, and fresh poultry blood may be consumed. In one of the more recent rounds of concern it was revealed that in many of the street markets in China birds are slaughtered and processed on site and in the open areas of the markets. There are no guidelines, and the scalding and picking fills the air with droplets and water vapor that can widely spread any harmful organisms.

Neither here nor abroad do the birds of small, independent producers represent the health risks that cramped, stressed, and rigidly confined poultry flocks do. Much is made of the supposed "bio-security" of modern confinement units, but ask any farmer you know if there really is such a thing as a bird- and rodent-free steel building. At the height of one avian flu scare a few years ago, a major hurricane roared through the South, breaking open scores of poultry buildings. Hundreds of thousands of badly stressed and controlled environment–dependent birds were dumped into a damaged environment. And this just as the major fall migration of wild birds was flowing into and across that region. I'm not a believer in conspiracy theories, but with all of those confinement-derived birds dumped into the environment, talk about avian flu went quickly away. Nor are six hens in a crate at a local bird market being subjected to the same harsh life and treatment as birds packed into a colony house or mega-cage unit. They are there for but a few hours, were generally caught up from feed and water earlier that morning, and will be back into new quarters before the day is over. As a countermeasure to *E. coli* problems, birds destined for harvest should be held off of feed for twenty-four hours to assure that they are processed with an empty digestive track. It is a mandated condition for on-farm processing in many states now.

Without markets to give the birds a measurable economic value and an outlet for surplus production the then-valueless birds will assuredly slip away into extinction. That appears to be the goal of some in the animal rights sector, but it is very much at odds with all of the work that has gone on in recent years to preserve and protect all the rare and heirloom breeding. There would have been no Renaissance without patrons and an economic undergirding to support those doing the actual work, and the same is now true of this poultry keeping renaissance of ours.

Consumers and producers alike will be best served by open and honest marketing options where the birds and the trading is open to all and open for all to see. Restrictive and unenlightened regulation will not serve this, but will drive out and then kill this form of marketing as it is still aborning.

With but a very few exceptions the species discussed in this book were never kept in great numbers. Their production and their initial use or sale was farm based. Demand hinged on exposure to and familiarity with them. Modern communication methods have expanded initial levels of exposure, but often without providing hard information in the needed levels and amounts. You can't learn poultry without getting a fair amount of mud and manure on you.

Over the years I have found a high level of enjoyment and pleasant anticipation in the earliest stages of developing an enterprise for our small farm. An extended period is needed to get things done right, to gather and process the basic knowledge necessary to be a good producer, to become familiar with markets both for foundation stock and commercial production, to establish facilities, and to locate sources for seedstock. The potential market is what will dictate ultimate flock size. Some markets can be grown, but don't start looking for barbecued pheasant legs or popcorn quail pieces at the next state fair.

Poultry ventures have a tendency to grow out of each other or to build one atop another. They can be invaluable in adding diversity to the farm enterprise mix, but care should be exercised to prevent the farm from becoming skewed too far toward the production of any single themed pursuit.

A poultry yard, the center for poultry production on a farm or small-holding, can and should hold and fully accommodate one, two, or three (maybe) poultry species. Yes, I too can name those who promote that they own breeds by the score and in more species than they have toes. Far more have gainfully devoted their time to work with just one species or even a single breed.

Poultry markets are often fast moving and might only present short selling windows each year. The hatchling market, for example, is very seasonal in nature. Here it flourishes for a few weeks beginning around the Easter holiday and winding down in early summer. A second, quite short window sometimes opens in early fall.

Some farm supply store chains kick off the spring with a Chix Day at which they may also offer some turkey poults and waterfowl hatchlings. There are in-store displays, poultry-themed promotions, and follow-up sales of feed and supplies where they make their real money. It is a cycle not unlike how Valentine's candy gives way to Easter candy in the big box stores. Folks hereabouts have learned to wait until these things wind down and then make lowball offers for the birds that have grown too large for the store displays. That is a market that farmers/breeders should not contemplate or seek to compete in as the goal is to quickly sell a lot of chicks to then make increased, longer term sales of feed and supplies. Though offered in fairly substantial numbers, the birds are offered in limited variety and are bred only to an "industrial" standard. And the misinformation that can flourish there is wondrous to behold. I previously mentioned seeing a store clerk "sex" baby ducks by lifting them up and eyeballing their foot size. He then assured the novice buyer that those little balls of fluff could then be taken home and released on a pond on a chill March afternoon. The manager of that particular store now keeps a watchful eye on me during their "chix" days. Let's just say that they don't like my store-aisle poultry seminars. My good wife doesn't like me going in there either, but that may be because I have been known to buy her anniversary gifts in places that sell stove bolts and baling twine.

Short marketing windows and modest levels of demand; these are niche markets of the first water. The knowledge behind them and the quality bred into them is what gives these alternative varieties their greatest value and largest returns to the producer.

It can be phrased a hundred different ways, but the question every farmer in a direct marketing situation had best be prepared to answer is, "What makes your production worth that?" I have stood answering that question for a half hour and more and then watched the folks amble away to buy other, cheaper birds. So often they are dead ducks going away to buy what will soon be some real dead ducks. When other producers ask me how to cope with this, I answer with something I read long ago in a magazine for independent grocers. It is a grain of wisdom that would almost fit on a bumper sticker: "I have no argument with one who sells his product for less than mine. For after all, who knows better what it is worth than the one who produced it?"

Not long ago a friend with a history with and a reputation for producing good waterfowl added a new breed of ducks for his area. From a single pair of Ancona ducks he sold $150 worth of ducklings hatched from eggs from their first few weeks of laying. Now $150 isn't heart transplant money, but those two little ducks netted more than a beef cow would in most years. And they cost much less to acquire and tend. My friend is a pragmatic sort and knew that their newness to his area and vivid coloring gave those ducklings a raised level of interest and added value. His position as an established waterfowl producer and his skills and abilities in breeding and rearing waterfowl are what gave them their greatest and most sustainable value.

From this little two-duck point A, my friend had decisions to make as to how to go up or down. The one sale was not the opening for creating a Ponderosa-sized duck ranch, but it does start one to thinking about what could be done with one or more of the many different duck breeds now available. My friend has opted to build a modest duck venture of a few breeding trios based on two breeds. The first is the Muscovy, a hardy variety that fares well in his region and has an established level of demand. It is a flock that can be tweaked by adding a different color variety or breeding up to somewhat larger birds. His early Ancona sales were fueled in fair measure by their newness in his area and the colorful nature of the ducklings, showing spotting early on. He could see this early interest and profit from it by rapidly moving through a number of different breeds, but chasing fads never builds a long-term market. Numbers can be bred up quickly to fill a geographical niche, and despite gimmicks like selling male or female offspring only they will spread widely eventually.

My friend Neal Gray's quest has become a search for a breed of duck with a distinctive appearance and the size and growth rate needed to have substantial table value. The bird should lay fairly well and produce an egg with a certain eye appeal, and it should be able to flourish in his southern climate. It is a lot to ask for from something that goes through life on two clown-like feet. He has bred one strain of geese for over thirty years. His skills, his proven facilities, and his standing as a trusted breeder of poultry will help him to expand the niche for the new duck breed of his choosing. He is working now with some ducks of the Appleyard breed and made a quite substantial investment in his initial stock, bought from another, highly regarded breeder.

The good ones in any breed or variety will stand out even to the most inexperienced. They look the part, but how they got there and how to keep them there will require the value-adding inputs that can be provided only by a knowledgeable and dedicated breeder.

I have been to enough bird markets to know to never pass by any coop or crate lest you miss a treasure that could be tucked away in its recesses. I have also learned that the best filled crates come from veteran producers that are far more than mere chicken keepers and traders. Such folks seldom sell their very best, but they often have birds to sell that can be used to breed up to better levels of conformation and performance.

I suspect that my friend will never sell a great number of ducklings from his two chosen breeds, but his birds will all be good ones. He will also have some additional income from selling hatching eggs, some started and adult breeders, and the sale of surplus males and culled breeding stock. During the hatching season you will not buy eggs from him for table egg prices, nor will he sell birds until the future needs of his flock are fully met with birds of the quality necessary to advance his flock.

One hundred ducklings at farm store prices will gross $400. One hundred ducklings at breeder prices will gross $750 to $1,500. With a continuing emphasis on quality it is conceivable that a truly select group of one hundred ducklings could gross $2,000 in small lot sales. The better they are, the fewer you have to sell to maintain a good cash stream.

The earning potential from small ventures will never be huge, but often the producer retains more of what is grossed. I would challenge anyone to develop, in rapid order, a single farm venture with the earning potential of ten to twelve small ventures grouped together and do so without putting the entire farm at risk from the failure of a single crop or market.

According to reports, a strong demand for poultry stock in forms other than hatchlings and hatching eggs is starting to emerge here and in other areas. Growing numbers of people have expressed a strong desire (backed with money) for birds well past the need for supplemental heat and special care that can be clearly sexed, are more fully showing breed character and type, and are still young enough to adapt readily to new facilities.

More and more people, even people farming extensively, are working away from home forty or more hours per week. When husband and wife are away so much livestock ventures must be able to function under reduced oversight. And many producers do not want to deal with the concern and care needed for surplus males.

By five to eight weeks of age most young fowl have been hardened off, are in good early feathering, and weaned away from supplemental heat. They are eating a complete grower/developer ration, type and feathering are clearly emerging, and sexing is becoming much easier. They are "started" birds and are highly desirable. And they are not priced cheaply. One hatchery is now selling seventeen-week-old chicken pullets for $14–$15 each from a very limited chice of breeds and with a shipping charge of $120.00 for just five such birds. I can hear many of you sputtering after reading that, but if they weren't selling them in goodly numbers would they be offering them and spending the money to promote their availability?

At local markets a five-to-eight-week-old pullet chick now sells for $5–$8 if it's of one of the more common breeds. A pullet at point-of-lay, eighteen to twenty-two weeks of age, will be priced at ten to sixteen dollars. Rarity, superior quality, and poultry of alternative varieties are price-increasing factors

It takes feed and space to grow out young birds in any number, and this is especially so with larger varieties such as turkeys or geese. Then, in the second half of each year, larger turkeys and waterfowl become a harder sell as buyers contemplate having to carry them through the upcoming winter before receiving any returns. Prices for started birds must fully cover all costs to produce them, provide for a fair return to producer labor, and offset the risks of slower demand as the year unwinds. With the production of started fowl it is the producer that has to contend with the matter of surplus males. One of the best marketing strategies that I have seen for dealing with this is to offer them only in breeding groups headed by one or two males. This means selling them as pairs, trios, or breeding pens of four to ten females and one or two males.

Buyers may balk a bit at first, but it is stand-your-ground time for producers. Explain that they are buying just one or two males instead of half or more of a box of as-hatched young, that they are being sold as breeding stock, that they are encouraging the propagation of their rare or heirloom variety, and that the young males have value on the table if not kept for breeding. I have had some customers continue to balk and insist that I sell them only females, which leaves me with one of two tacks to follow. The first is to say that the coop price remains the same with or without the male in it. At a couple of swaps I have sold the same male two or three times and still taken him back home with me. Or, if the customer has been especially belligerent, female prices will go up enough to cover the cost of a couple of males and enough more to cover my aggravation.

Most alternative poultry markets are going to be quite local in nature. Most of your sales will be within your state's borders and often within just an hour or two's drive from the home farm. The producer has to know that area, the people, what they want, and what they can and cannot pay for it. A friend with peafowl related that in one of his best years he sold 150 birds. An acquaintance with turkeys met near disaster with eight hundred birds to market. An Amish neighbor with range broilers had to quit production as demand grew to threaten his very way of life. Friends with pigeons consider it a very good day when they sell twenty to thirty birds at the local farmers' market. Each producer will have to find his or her own answer to the numbers question, but small, tight, and super good would seem the way to go in most instances.

Consumers for a fifty- or sixty-dollar young, heirloom tom turkey don't pass by every day. And you may have to give a brace of squabs with every ten broilers for many months before even beginning to build a market. With six hundred quail eggs in the incubator on the tenth day you don't need the nearby shooting preserve to tell you they found 'em cheaper.

Too often I have seen people sent home with alternative or exotic fowl with little more than a brief word of thanks. And I have also seen some mighty big checks change hands with the next words from the new owner being "What do I feed them?" Part of positioning oneself as a dependable supplier of birds worth the money is a willingness and a system to share what one knows about the birds being offered. I had been in the hog business for many years when I bought a young boar that essentially came with an owners' manual. At first I said "Yeah, right," threw it on the pickup dash, and drove home. A day or two later, while watching that old pig adjust to his new home, a question did come to mind. Out to the pickup I went and there, in a few simply written pages, was a bit of the hog's history, an outline of the care he had been given, and some suggestions on how to bring him into service. And at the bottom of that list was that all-important home phone number for questions the guide sheets did not answer.

Production agriculture has turned a very big corner in recent days, and we can no longer assume that everyone is on the same page as to skill set and experience. There are a lot of new "rurban" types on the scene as well as old hands trying new things, and relatively little in the way of supporting infrastructure has yet to form around these alternative poultry varieties.

Many people, for example, who want some "green-headed" ducks for their "lake" know and think only of Mallards. Flying Mallards will require special permits, will have to be pinioned to stay in one place, and only half of them have green heads and only for a certain part of each year. There are other green-headed ducks available to them, including Rouens, Appleyards, and Gray Calls, but most folks know little or nothing about them. And heaven protect you from those folks whose only source of knowledge is a single copy of a catalog from one of the larger hatcheries.

For many years I have helped with the poultry displays at one of the nation's largest shows and seminars for small farmers and thus have been a part of three solid days of teaching about poultry. I might speak with one person or couple a dozen times before they made the decisions to buy a fifty-dollar trio of chickens or pair of ducks. The questions they asked ranged from the most rudimentary to being so far out in left field that they baffled all poultry hands there. You will see these customers at last make the decision to buy when that one question that has so nagged them is finally answered and not before then.

A modern poultry venture is best "grown" not by building numbers but by increasing the quality of and the roles for the birds. Phyllis and I found a niche with some of the poultry breeds with a history of production on the family farms of the Midwest. A legendary poultryman in northern Missouri has keyed in on producing white egg–laying breeds of the Mediterranean class of large fowl chickens for decades.

There is a fly-by-night thing going on with poultry sales right now that many are finding disconcerting. "Pop-up hatcheries" frequently appear on the Internet offering all manner of birds and hatching eggs. Generally they take an order, skim their returns from an inflated price, and pass the order on to a larger hatchery for drop shipment of hatchlings or eggs to the buyer. Sadly, I also know people who have been burned and quite badly by high-profile individual producers. This has all come about just as growing numbers of buyers are gaining somewhat in awareness and are looking for something beyond "hatchery run" birds of what is termed an industrial type.

When birds of truly good type are set down at a market or farm exhibition, the one thing I hear more and more is "Ours don't look like that." People are confused by them, feel resentment that they were sold something lesser, or are turned back in their confusion and uncertainty.

A few weeks back, with our breeding pens set for the year, I took a few surplus Buff Orpington young males to our local farmers' market. The better ones were still back home, but the birds I brought still drew the "What are they?" and "Look how big they are!" comments. Sadly, I had to note that those young roosters were bought by a meat buyer rather than going home with any of those who said that they weren't like the ones they had back home.

Chickens, ducks, geese, pigeons—all can be made better by selective breeding, but that "Oh, it's just a chicken or a duck or a whatever" mentality has to be overcome. It is interesting to note that, at the bigger poultry events in our area, the birds that sell for the highest prices have either come in from the longest distances or are going to be taken away a substantial distance. Now I am not going to quote the Bible about a prophet in his own land, and I do notice that the better breeders here do not back down from a bird or birds that can make their flocks better. I know it sounds like I am contradicting myself here a bit, as I wrote earlier about the better-bred stock being recognizable and valued accordingly. Quality is still best recognized and valued accordingly by those who have drunk at the trough of experience. A great many producers are still learning to recognize and appreciate the good birds only after having some very agonizing experiences with the other kind. Most painful to see is a family with 4-H youngsters working their way through the mishmash that comes with birds they were told were good. Or a potential meat or egg producer finding out that he or she has invested in scattershot genetics that do not breed true and are putting offspring on the ground with a great deal of inconsistency to them. Or the beginning breeder who loses a year or more when dearly bought and long-awaited birds simply unwind before their eyes. Or someone with a lot of money invested in birds that are the absolute wrong fit for the intended task.

Poultry varieties cannot be thrown together willy-nilly in the poultry yard. Different species have different needs as to housing and feedstuffs, and they may even need some protection from each other. Perhaps the idea that the different poultry species can peacefully commingle comes from the Broadway musical *Oklahoma*, the lyrics of which describe a barnyard filled with "chicks and ducks and geese," but the image of the big red barn filled with all manner of livestock, happy and thriving, is pure myth. Wild-ranging and free-roosting birds can foul feedstuffs and equipment, hatchlings don't last long under stomping hooves of large stock, breedings cannot be controlled or even kept pure, health matters may suffer, and all manner of critters other than man have a taste for the fatted hen or turkey. And "it just don't look good," as my Scotch-Irish grandmother would say.

Just as a good workshop is made a more pleasant area to work by having a place for everything and everything in its place, so, too, is the poultry yard. On our not-quite three acres over the years, we have kept pigeons, large-fowl chickens, bantams, pheasants, ducks, geese, and turkeys—not all at the same time and certainly not all in the same confines. We operate with a system of small pens, sun porches, breeding coops, and covered runs. There, in the past six months, you would have found ducks, pigeons, a few bantams, several breeds of large-fowl chickens, and even a trio of turkeys. The ducks were a rescue project of sorts, but, to paraphrase that old movie line, "Feed them well, and they will reproduce." Some of the equipment in use is old, and some began life meant for other uses such as rabbit raising or kennel use. There are some high-dollar birds eating and drinking out of tuna cans, and on my hands and arms are the scars of decades of "wire rash." The work is about the birds and breeding them better, and I'm still like a kid on Christmas morning every time I pull a tray of new hatchlings from the incubator.

About us now are a new group of poultry folks, neither fanciers nor hobbyists, but those reaching back to the golden age of poultry production to bring forward the birds, the thinking, and the practices that made that era truly golden. They owe a debt to those who have kept so many different poultry varieties alive for the last three-quarters of a century. They are paying back that debt by putting those birds back to work.

Five Brown Chinese geese, a pair and a trio of Royal Palm turkeys, a dozen pair of Carneau pigeons, a quaking line of ten to twenty Runner ducks, fifty Wyandotte hens, or even a combination of these do not a big business make, But they do fit into a place that has rightfully been theirs for a very long time. For some it may be possible to grow their numbers beyond these levels, well beyond them perhaps. Yet when held in even the most modest of numbers, there can be much worth in these birds. The ability to put four dozen duck eggs on the table at the farmers' market each Saturday may be what draws new buyers, holds old ones, and clearly testifies that you are about something more than being just one more of a cookie-cutter crowd of peddlers.

Pricing poultry, especially poultry of the less familiar varieties, is never simple. Certainly, the selling price must cover all the costs to produce, including everything from energy costs to equipment depreciation to producer labor. Any convenience, such as starting the birds, adds to value, as does the backing of a skilled and knowledgeable producer ready and willing to advise and counsel.

Whenever possible I like to buy started fowl or even younger adult birds. They can be brought into production much sooner, and with some age on them it is far easier to evaluate both the merits and the faults of individual birds. A case can nearly always be made for buying even a high-dollar trio over a box of fifteen to twenty-five as-hatched youngsters. Out of such numbers you would expect to raise and then cull down to one pretty good trio and possibly no more than two or three backup birds of somewhat lesser quality. It will then be a year or more before those youngsters will be fully developed and ready to go into production. Granted, started or adult birds are not easy to find, but few are the times that I've seen a trip to the state fair, a trip to a poultry show of any size, or a call to the Poultry Improvement Program at the state department of agriculture that did not produce several leads within a reasonable driving distance.

As people begin to gain in experience with poultry, they are better able to see and understand the pricing of poultry stock of good quality, real flock-building birds. Fifty dollars may sound high to some for a single, but at one time three-figures prices were not uncommon for better-bred birds. Nor is it really high now when placed in comparison to thousand-dollar-per-head feeder calves, farm ground passing five figure prices per acre, and fifteen-dollar-a-bag poultry feed. A female of most poultry species will, if given good care, produce herself many times over, often for a good many years to come. Egg production will generally decline by about 10–15 percent for each year after the first or second year of laying, but there are geese, for example, that have produced fertile eggs for over two decades.

Rarity and improved breeding background, though of substantial value, do not come with any sort of easy-to-use pricing guide. When in the purebred hog business we grew to rely on an old rule of thumb that held that a young male of good breeding type had an initial value of at least two to three times that of a young meat animal of good market weight. I think you can price avian seedstock similarly based on a few simple points of reasoning. First, it takes a relatively few good birds to produce many more of that ilk if they are given good care. Second, is a now widely understood truth that the good ones simply do not just happen. It takes much time, effort, and investment to produce them. Third, producers at the higher levels have never been overly abundant (it is not a calling for the faint of spirit and character).

Second only to "How much must I pay" is the question of how many such birds are needed? How many can a producer reasonably expect to sell? A reading of the old literature turns up, from time to time, a recommended number of large fowl to be produced yearly or seasonally that may still be good. Many times the number one hundred is presented as an early goal in the marketing for species such as turkeys, waterfowl, or guineas. Granted, multiples of ten always make for simpler calculations, and we all like to think in terms of nice, round numbers. Still, that number has merit, at least in the early going for most alternative poultry ventures. It is a number that is doable without great expenditures, and it will challenge the producer to reach beyond his or her comfort zone both in skill building and marketing. Few of us know a hundred people who will buy a sixty-five-dollar turkey just because we raised it in a certain way. A sixty-five-dollar goose, a twenty-dollar duck, a fifteen-dollar roasting fowl, or an eight-dollar brace of quail—none of those are in an everyday food budget right now. Most producers will have to build to that one hundred bird point in increments of, say, fifteen to twenty-five birds before moving to a lot of fifty and then, maybe, one hundred.

It involves building a close-to-the-vest customer list, and should anyone be lost from such a list they may be lost forever. Such buyers are generally quite exacting in what they want, and it is a transaction that involves far more than the exchange of feathered stock for paper dollars. They are going to host the feast, but the producer is going to have to stock the menu, know the cooking methods, and be prepared to catch the blame if things go wrong. You are setting out to do business with people who read *Food & Wine*, donate to PBS, and trust Martha Stewart. They may not ask which member of Plymouth Colony first carved an ancestor of your turkey, but you can bet that some have thought about it.

That one hundred bird figure is, the more I ponder it, a most important mile marker for which to aim. Costs and risks won't be that great, and once it has been reached the learning curve will be reduced and future courses of action should appear much clearer.

In pondering the issues in poultry production now, the one that still seems cause for much confusion is the question of exactly what is and isn't range production.

Aside from adult and well-started geese and some ducks at later stages of development, most fowl are not grazers. Putting them out "on grass" to pare feed bills is not going to work and may even cause some problems of its own. Birds forced to consume too much greenery or plant material that is too long and fibrous may actually suffer and die with bound crops. The crop of choice for poultry rearing back when nearly all poultry production was done out of doors was bluegrass. It was kept trimmed short, is narrow leafed, is easily consumed in small snips by the birds, and is fine textured. And with most species, it had a very limited role to play in their levels of nutrition. For optimum performance, birds on range should continue to receive a full feeding of the rations appropriate for their age and stage of development.

The true benefits to birds on range are abundant sunshine, greater access to soil mineralization, feathering benefits derived from access to dew and light rain, a more stimulating environment, access to insects for a more varied diet, and muscle tone (meat texture) improved by greater levels of exercise. The leg and thigh muscles, quick twitch muscles and some of the most important "money" cuts in poultry, benefit from more use. Both taste and texture is improved in range-raised birds that are bred for the range.

Range rearing can and will slow down the grow-out period. The birds will be on the farm or smallholding somewhat longer and may consume more feed as a result. It produces a premium product, but there will often be added cost factors with that production. At the very best, costs to produce on range are awash with the costs to produce per pound in confinement. And a wet or cool spell can push costs and losses dramatically if even but a few days in duration. I realize that I have rained on a lot of parades with this, but what the birds are and their limits have to be respected whether they are being raised on range or in a controlled environment facility. We are talking here about creatures that consume but a few ounces of feed each per day, and you cannot starve a profit out of a living creature.

The one true way to work on reducing feed costs is to pare out the poor performers and boost production from the good ones with improved levels of nutrition. Too often a small flock of poultry is set up and allowed to just putter along until it is ended by producer disinterest or natural attrition.

To put the best performers to work you are going to have to get out among them and take them in hand to most fully evaluate them as individuals. The hard truth is that a lot of high-priced feed is going into some poor or even nonperforming birds; on too many holdings a surplus of males and old birds are being fed because no one knows what to do with them, and a great many birds of very poor quality have been allowed to breed on and damage some already gravely endangered gene pools.

There must be more in the way of understanding of these birds, their historical uses, and the practical limits to their uses and applications. I can remember standing in a treeline, over fifty years ago, watching a flock of about 1,500 Bronze turkeys work their way through a series of small, inter-connected fields here in eastern Missouri. The fields would be used for a single summer and early fall to grow out the birds and then be turned back to row crop production for a period of at least three years. It was a spin on the old McLean County system of raising hogs outdoors and was used to prevent parasite buildups and break down disease cycles in the soil.

Not far away in the same township a modest-sized chicken laying house stood atop gently rolling hills. The house and lot were used the year around, year after year to contain a flock of two hundred to three hundred Leghorn laying hens. It worked because the birds were kept loose housed and in modest numbers. They were day ranged and had little stress, they were very well fed and tended, and the house was cleaned often. The gentle slope grew very little in the way of greenery, but each rain did lift up and wash the surface wastes into a strip of sod below the hill where the runoff was very effectively filtered.

Poultry species have been kept in a number of different systems with good results, as long as the birds are kept comfortable and secure. The previous examples are but two from a time when the first great cycle of U.S. poultry production was winding down.

A new course is unfolding now, one that may be even more varied in its nature and construct. It will hinge on ever greater levels of interaction between producer and consumer, however. Opportunities may boil down to being the supplier of specialty fowl to a handful of nearby restaurants, running an old-fashioned egg route into a nearby pocket of urban sprawl, producing the green eggs or holiday turkeys for a cooperative-supplied CSA, working with one or two traditional breeds supplying seedstock and hatching eggs, providing the "white doves" for local events, or us-ing something novel and colorful and feathered to draw consumers to other production of your farm or smallholding. More likely, it will be a combination of two or three such ventures that will be at least somewhat interconnected.

The mix of ventures and the role they will play will vary from farm to farm. What has worked for us will not work for others, and others may have need for poultry ventures we have never considered. Fads will come and go, dietary trends are ever changing, and the markets for all food items are always going to be at least partially cost driven

It is not often stated coldly in print, but one element of this poultry surge of ours is only going to be here for a while before it is apt to move on to something else. A lot of the boost in demand for alternative poultry varieties has come from people with substantial disposable income who are spending at least some of it on poultry and poultry keeping. They may want to have at least a little control over what goes on the family table, have a desire to give the kids a bit of a hands-on lesson about nature, or are pursuing one more trendy pastime.

Not long ago the Sunday *St. Louis Post-Dispatch* listed ten gift suggestions for Mother's Day. Among them was a backyard chicken house with the capacity of a handful of hens and costing just a few dollars less than a grand. Now I'm not implying that Mom isn't deserving of nice gifts, but among her greatest treasures is your handprint in a disc of plaster of Paris that you made years ago in Sunday school. I only gave twenty-five dollars for my first car, and a thousand-dollar chicken house for a six-pack of hens has fad written all over it.

What has to—and I believe is beginning to—emerge is a core and a corps of real, old-school poultry farmer/breeders. They are not working huge numbers—that is a rather recent phenomenon in production agriculture—but they are keeping their birds for the long haul and to be a true business. They watch trends, know which breeds are hot, and are looking beyond the kitsch and the smarmy photographs of chickens in clothing that cloud the scene now.

E ditors tell me that I have a problem with not knowing when to put in the last period and turn off the old typewriter.

What I have tried to do here is not so much present a full-on how-to book or breed encyclopedia but rather address the alternative poultry scene of the moment and what should be done to continue, long-term, with the opportunities it represents. It is production that industrial agriculture and the agribiz boys at the state colleges thought had been lost in the dustbin of history.

In a far corner of north St. Louis County in the 1930s, my grandparents bought a small parcel of pre-subdivision land. With the help of a modest laying flock and a small flock of Pekin ducks, they weathered a depression and a world war in which most protein sources were extensively rationed. Often they bartered eggs and a roasting duck for milk and butter and similar products from their like-minded neighbors.

The better part of a century passed before opportunities in small-flock alternative poultry production came again. If we muff it this time, I doubt that they will ever come again. Too many of the remaining gene pools will simply go over the abyss due to neglect and discouragement.

You will not be made a good and lasting producer of these birds just by owning lots of them. The real need of most of these birds is not that there be more of them but that they be held in a lot more hands.

Two trios of well-bred turkeys can make you a real player in this game. If, as many knowledgeable folks are predicting and the economic signs are indicating, we are moving into a new era of small, artisanal, and even micro-farms, the demand for poultry and small stock varieties is only going to grow.

Most of us started with hand-me-down birds or birds bought from a catalog in a price special offer. I saved pennies and nickels for some of the first birds I bought, and my idea of the perfect birthday or Christmas gift would arrive with air holes in the box.

You soon learn that, in the poultry game, there are the so-so birds and the really good ones and not a lot in between. That knowledge and the move to own and breed from the good ones separate the dabbler from the poultry hand. If you're not moving in that direction, you are the limit to any success to which you might aspire.

The voice of the turtledove's domestic cousin is to be heard again in the land. Along with it will sound the quacking of ducks, the hissing and honking of geese, the gobbling of turkeys, and the clucking of many, many hens. It is also the time for producers to form the plans and select the varieties that will enable them to build profitable and lasting enterprise mixes for their farms and smallholdings.

INDEX